# animal
# variety

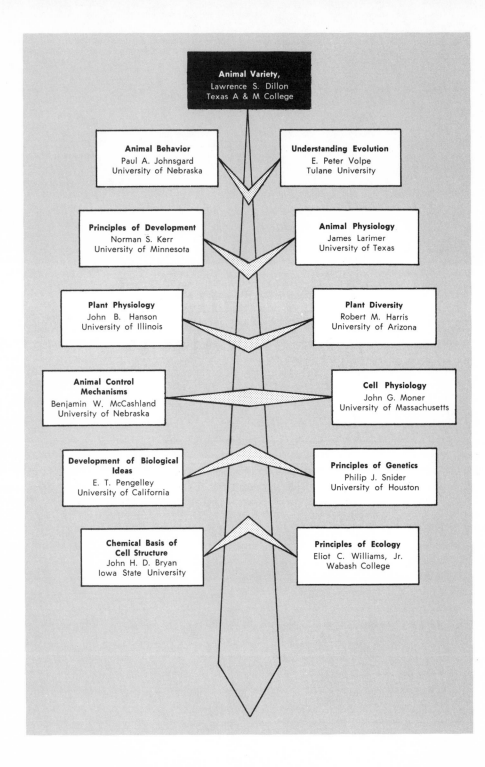

Biology today is in the midst of profound and exciting revelations. This has resulted in a spectacular surge of biological knowledge and the consequent need for new approaches to the teaching of biology. The **Concepts of Biology Series,** designed for the introductory course, transmits the excitement of biology to the college student seeking a liberal education. The underlying theme of each book in the series is to foster an awareness of biology as an imaginative, evolving science. While the individual titles are self-contained, collectively they comprise a modern synthesis of major biological principles.

# animal
# variety

LAWRENCE S. DILLON
*Professor of Biology*
*Texas A&M University*

**WM. C. BROWN COMPANY PUBLISHERS**
*Dubuque, Iowa*

*Manufactured by*
WM. C. BROWN CO. INC., Dubuque, Iowa
Printed in U. S. A.

# Preface

This book is designed to serve in introductory biology and zoology courses both as supplementary reading and, in conjunction with other specialized titles, to supplant the usual bound volume. To maintain brevity and yet satisfy the demands of the two objectives, the morphological characteristics of the various taxa are as far as possible condensed to diagrams and tables. Actual descriptive matter is thus confined to amplification of the more obscure details, while the remaining text is freed to present the major fabric of diversification woven by the course of animal evolution.

Since every phylum and other principal taxon of animals possesses one or more peculiarities that set it apart from all others, consistency in presentation is considered detrimental rather than an asset. Frequently the distinctions may be of a morphological nature, but on as many occasions they may be behavioral or functional. In one group, the larvae may form the basis for diversification, while in another, the life cycle may provide the major feature. To bring out the principal paths of evolution, the treatment varies with the nature of the immediate taxon.

Wherever suitable intermediate forms exist, too, the steps followed during the phylogenetic history of a taxon in acquiring its specializations are indicated, in order that the student may gain a fuller appreciation both of the individual taxa and of their kinships with others. And finally, the processes of evolution as a whole, as well as its basic principles, interweave the entire discussion to present the animals as living organisms, responding day by day to immediate stimuli and becoming altered over long periods of geological time as changing conditions demanded.

Many persons have assisted in the preparation of this work. Photographs and other illustrative matter have been borrowed from many sources, which are more appropriately acknowledged individually in the captions. However, special thanks are given to Dr. William G. Degenhardt for his generosity in supplying a number of his personal photographs of reptiles, amphibians, and mammals. To the artist, Peter Loewer, the author is also indebted for the care and skill with which the original figures have been prepared. In reviewing the entire manuscript, Dr. Edward J. Kormondy, of Oberlin College, contributed a number of helpful suggestions, and his thoughtfulness and careful analysis are greatly appreciated. And finally, to his wife, who has typed the manuscript and collaborated fully throughout its completion, he is more grateful than he can possibly state here.

# Contents

# CHAPTER 1

# The origin of life and beginnings of diversity

Living things as a whole are so unlike other physical objects that, throughout most of mankind's history, life has been viewed as a mysterious force whose origin and nature were entirely beyond human comprehension. As the chemical constitution of organisms was explored, however, it became increasingly clear that living matter, or protoplasm, is constructed of the same elements as nonliving and that the ordinary principles of chemistry apply equally to all things. Only the specific compounds that compose living matter were found to be distinct from those of the inorganic world. At first such *organic* chemicals were thought incapable of being produced artificially, but after Wöhler prepared urea in the test tube, this concept, too, rapidly gave way as one after another of the organics were synthesized.

However, the formulation of the most complex organic compound is still widely remote from even the beginnings of an understanding of life's origin. First a knowledge had to be gained of the intertwining chemical reactions that supply the cell with energy, new protoplasm, and its other requirements. But here we need not be concerned with the intricacies of the metabolic processes, only with the current theories of how the necessary organic substances may have arisen from inorganic sources. Then, after they have been reviewed, it can be conjectured how living things themselves may have come into existence from these basic materials and began to diversify.

## I. THE ORIGIN OF LIFE'S MATERIALS

In the final analysis, organisms require three basic types of organic materials in order to function. The first of these, *energy producers* in the form of compounds which can readily be oxidized to supply energy, is among the prime requisites. Whereas higher animals need carbohydrates and fats to meet their energy requirements, unicellular forms frequently can employ such simple compounds as formic and acetic acids and various alcohols for this purpose.

Because the foregoing class of materials is chiefly of value only when expended, its members contribute little of a permanent nature. The major constituents of protoplasm are the second basic type of material, the complex compounds known as *proteins* that comprise nearly 80 per cent of the cell's total organic content. Besides forming fibers and other structural parts, many serve as enzymes, those catalysts whose presence is needed wherever a metabolic reaction takes place.

The third great class of required compounds are the *nucleic acids,* long chainlike molecules composed of nucleotides which will be described later. Two major varieties exist, ribonucleic acid (RNA), which contains the sugar ribose, and deoxyribonucleic acid (DNA), which contains deoxyribose instead; both are essential in the formation of new proteins. In addition, their basic constituents, the nucleotides, serve in many fundamental capacities. One nucleotide known as adenosine triphosphate (ATP) is particularly important in the storage of the energy liberated by energy-producing compounds. It is this class of material and the two foregoing, then, whose origins need to be considered.

### Conditions of Primitive Times

Although no theory of the earth's origin is universally accepted, it is generally conceded that the earth for long eons during its early history was a glowing sphere. Only after the crust had cooled sufficiently could water vapor condense and fill the hollows of the surface to form the oceans. Since nothing living could possibly have survived the high temperatures of the earlier period, these waters were obviously sterile — a point that is of utmost importance to current concepts of life's origins.

In addition to that condition of the seas, one other feature of the primitive earth has particular bearing in this discussion, the probable difference between the primordial atmosphere and that of today. Carbon dioxide was in all likelihood present in large quantities, whereas free oxygen may have been nearly absent. Moreover, carbon monoxide was apparently more abundant than now, and a considerable fraction of the air possibly was made up of ammonia ($NH_3$), methane ($CH_4$), and hydrogen sulfide ($H_2S$). While such an atmosphere might be fatal to modern land animals, it seems to have been fundamental to the creation of the compounds of which all living things are composed.

## Energy Producers

During the last several decades, methods have been developed and demonstrated in the laboratory suggestive of means by which energy sources may have come into existence in nature.[1] Many of the first attempts employed such organic compounds as methane, ethane, and ethylene as the starting point, combining them with chlorine or other active elements, as in the following example:

$$CH_4 \quad + \quad Cl_2 \quad \longrightarrow \quad CH_3Cl \quad + \quad HCl$$

| Methane | Chlorine | Methyl chloride | |

$$CH_3Cl \quad + \quad H_2O \quad \longrightarrow \quad CH_3OH \quad + \quad HCl$$

Methyl alcohol

Since alcohols serve as energy producers for a number of organisms, this method of synthesis possibly represents one origin of the compounds. Because they involve gases, the reactions could have occurred in the atmosphere, their products sifting down to the earth and reaching the seas with subsequent rains. Today any organic compound of this sort deposited in the oceans is quickly attacked by micro-organisms and broken into its constituent parts, but, under the sterile conditions of primitive times, it could have survived indefinitely.

Another approach to the problem makes use of high energy rays. For example, Dr. M. Calvin of the University of California, Berkeley, employed a cyclotron to irradiate solutions of carbon dioxide in water. At first he obtained formic acid, but, with additional irradiation, this simple compound gave rise to some fairly complex carbohydrates. Since atomic

---

[1]For a full discussion of this topic, refer to A. I. Oparin, *The Origin of Life on Earth*, 3rd ed., New York: Academic Press, 1957. The first chapter of this reference provides a fascinating account of ancient, medieval, and more modern concepts of life's origin. J. Keosian, *The Origin of Life*, New York: Reinhold Publishing Corporation, 1964, presents a brief but thorough summary of present hypotheses.

energy from the sun, as well as ultraviolet rays from the same source, are amply available in the atmosphere, especially at high elevations, similar reactions undoubtedly could have occurred on the primitive earth, and their products, after reaching the seas, could have accumulated in ever-increasing concentrations with the passing millenia.

### The Formation of Proteins

Because synthesis of proteins involves two distinct steps, the production of this class of compounds is somewhat more complex than that of the energy providers. First the amino acids must be created, and, second, these compounds need to be linked together by the hundreds or thousands to form the actual proteins. The unit amino acids can be created rather simply in the laboratory under conditions that may simulate those of the early earth. Three of the constituents of the conjectured primitive atmosphere, ammonia, water, and carbon dioxide, readily unite to produce ammonium carbonate, an inorganic chemical of frequent commercial use. If a quantity of this compound is exposed to a high-energy source, such as an electric spark, atomic rays, X-rays, or utlraviolet light, analysis of the treated substance reveals that most of the amino acids have been synthesized. Had a bolt of lightning, for example, passed through some of this substance suspended in the atmosphere, as must have happened innumerable times during earth's long history, amino acids could have been created in quantity. After their formation, these compounds, like the energy producers, sifted down to the surface and eventually accumulated in the oceans.

Although an accumulation of amino acids in the seas can readily be conjectured to have been produced by this or some similar process, these compounds cannot become coupled to one another under natural conditions as long as they remain in solution. To bring about their union by natural processes, several proposals have been advanced. One of these begins by demonstrating that when solutions of amino acids are evaporated the resulting film contains short chains of amino acids, called polypeptides. In comparable fashion during primitive times the oceanic solutions may frequently have washed upon rocks during storms and high tides and left films to be dried by the sun. Later under similar periods of high water, these films could have washed back into the seas. During endless repetitions of the processes, the polypeptide chains, too, could have united to one another, and, thus building up chains of increasing length, gradually became full-fledged proteins. The seas in this manner were made brothlike by the slowly increasing concentrations of proteinaceous materials.

## The Formation of Nucleic Acids

As stated earlier, the two kinds of nucleic acids are in reality long chains of nucleotides; the latter in turn are combinations of certain pentose sugars and phosphates together with a base. The base may be either a pyrimidine or a purine, both of which are closely akin chemically and, like amino acids, consist of nitrogen as well as oxygen, hydrogen, and carbon. The chief difference between them and the amino acids is that their carbon and nitrogen atoms are arranged in one or two rings.

Since these bases resemble the amino acids in chemical composition, it is no surprise to find that they can be synthesized in the same manner. It has now been established that the very same spark of electricity, which on passing through a tube of ammonium carbonate creates amino acids, forms all the typical purines and pyrimidines simultaneously. What still remains unknown are the mechanisms by which these compounds are coupled to the pentose sugar and phosphate to form the nucleotides, as well as those which enable the nucleotide units to become coupled into the actual nucleic acids.

## II. THE ORIGIN OF LIVING THINGS

Undoubtedly problems still exist in the theoretical aspects of creating the fundamental ingredients of living protoplasm, yet enough has now been accomplished to demonstrate that these raw materials could have come into existence naturally, beginning with simple inorganic and organic compounds. What is not at all clear is the methods by which the complex products combined into even the simplest possible kind of functional unit which might be considered a living cell.

The lack of any generally accepted explanation of life's origin stems, of course, from man's inability to perform experiments of sufficient complexity to bring about the union of all ingredients. Conjecture alone is possible at the moment. Hence, it should be realized, not only that the following account is entirely hypothetical, but also that it is only one of many current theories on the subject.

Basically the brief concept presented here is built upon viruses, the only known objects which possess properties of both living and nonliving substances. Consequently, many biologists view them as possibly representing some of the steps involved in the formation of actual organisms. Because the viruses cannot multiply outside living cells, other scientists believe them to be degenerate bacterialike organisms or particles from more advanced cells. To avoid entering the argument, here they will not be treated as the actual descendants of intermediate steps but as mere suggestions of stages that may have occurred.

Among the first steps that began the transition of the oceanic broth into life was a chance association between a cluster of identical protein molecules and one of RNA, as suggested by the smallest known virus, one called $\phi\chi174$ which attacks bacteria. In this association the nucelotide arrangement in the RNA necessarily corresponded to the sequence of amino acids in the protein; hence, these two types of complementary molecules were able to reproduce themselves and build up large populations in the seas. Although self-reproducing, this chemical association was not alive, for it was totally dependent upon the seas for its organic compounds, including ATP.

After this fortuitous origin, it can be visualized that over the long eons of geologic time the processes of molecular diversification began. Among some later descendants the molecules increased in size, and still later, by failing to separate after duplication, others made gains in the number of molecules present. At any rate, among the RNA viruses of plants and animals, there is a long series of types suggestive of these steps. After the passage of more time, a lipid coat was added around the protein, which now was arranged as a cylindrical shell enclosing the RNA. Still later, when a considerable complexity had been gained, molecules of DNA became associated with the RNA core, perhaps providing greater stability in the genetical processes. Many bacteriophages, viruses that parasitize bacteria, are among the simpler types showing this kind of organization.

Instead of the simple tubular condition described above, many viruses of animals are of much greater complexity, being constructed of several alternating layers of proteins and lipids together with a nucleic acid core. Still others, like the rickettsias, approach the smallest bacteria in size; so not too much of a gap exists between them and the simplest known living cells. But like the very first ones, all these preliving stages were dependent upon an external source for their amino acids and ATP, the seas serving for them as live cells do now for the viruses. How internal sources of supply were developed cannot even be guessed at present. Consequently it is apparent, that, while much has been gained toward an understanding of how life may have come into existence on the earth, there are still many important steps to be explored by biologists of the future.

No matter how fallacious the above hypothetical account may ultimately prove to be, one thing is evident — even before life itself in a strict sense came into existence, the progenitory stock of necessity exhibited the ability to diversify; otherwise the stepwise transition of the brothlike seas into true organisms could never have been accomplished. Diversification ever since the advent of life has been one of the outstanding properties of living things. The contribution this attribute has made to animal life is the theme of the following pages.

CHAPTER **2**

# Animal diversity and relationships

Back in the days of the early Greek philosophers, it was quite a simple matter to become familiar with all the diversification that existed among what were then considered to be animals. In the first place, the life of only a relatively small part of the globe was known in those times. And secondly, just actively moving creatures, like worms, insects, crabs, spiders, fish, birds, and mammals, were classed as animals. Such things as corals, sponges, and other sessile organisms were placed in a distinct category called the Zoophyta by Aristotle. This group, whose name means "animal-plants," was separated from both animals and plants, being viewed as intermediate between those two types.

This simple arrangement persisted throughout most of the Middle Ages, until two sets of events suddenly upset the world of biologists. One set consisted of the extensive explorations into previously unknown corners of the world, which brought to light many living things completely unknown to the Greek fathers of biology. But the second, the advent and development of the microscope, was even more disturbing, for the new world of life that this instrument opened, disclosed a seemingly unending variety of new organisms, whose existence previously never had been so much as suspected.

## I. EARLY SCHEMES OF CLASSIFICATION

Even after two centuries and more of world and microscopic explorations, relatively little of the extent of variation among animals had become apparent. When Carl Linné, the father of the modern system

8

of classification, first published his outline of animal nomenclature in 1758, he included names and descriptions of all the animals then known — a total of about 4,000 species were described in the 700 pages of his volume. Because the extent of variation was both unknown and unappreciated, he grouped all of these into six *classes* — not phyla, it should be noted, as the latter category did not come into use until a considerable number of years later. It is interesting to observe that in his scheme he continued the early superficiality of his forerunners, for his six major subdivisions consisted of the Mammalia, Aves, Amphibia, Pisces, Insecta, and Vermes — four for the vertebrates and only two for all the invertebrates, including the unicellular forms.

But one must bear in mind that in those days, the early concepts of *abiogenesis*[1] were still prevalent to some extent. Hence the attitude existed, that, if worms and microscopic life could arise from muck or in fermenting broths, their form and structure certainly could hold very little of real significance.

However, a somewhat better appreciation of the invertebrates came even before Pasteur's studies in 1862 forever ended the notions of spontaneous generation. These advances were provided by the then new science of paleontology, the study of fossil organisms, because invertebrates occur in far greater variety in the rocky strata of the earth than do the vertebrates. The first advances were provided by two French paleontologists and zoologists, J. B. Lamarck in 1809 and 1815 and G. Cuvier in 1816 and 1829. In Cuvier's scheme of classification, the invertebrates were separated from the vertebrates and then subdivided into three classes. To accomplish this, the annelids and almost all the arthropods were united under the name Articulata and the brachiopods and barnacles were placed in the Mollusca, while the remaining invertebrates were classed as the Radiata, including many, of course, which were not radiate. Lamarck's scheme went even further and established many more invertebrate classes — ten in his earlier and twelve in his later version. His classes included the Mollusca, Cirripedia (barnacles), Annelida, Crustacea, Arachnida, Insecta, Infusoria (rotifers and some protozoans), Polypes (sponges, polypoid coelenterates, and certain protozoans), Radiata (jellyfish, ctenophores, and echinoderms), Vermes (flukes, tapeworms, roundworms, and a few earthworms), Tunicata, and Conchifera (ostracods, brachiopods, and certain mollusks). In spite of Lamarck's scheme being vastly superior, that of Cuvier was more widely accepted and dominated zoological thinking until about 1850.

---

[1]The theory that living things arise spontaneously from mud, offal, slime, decaying flesh, and the like.

Since the latter date, studies on the embryology and life history of the many forms, as well as on their cytology and habits, have gradually contributed to a better understanding of the relationships of the great variety of animal life now known. Similarly more detailed researches on morphology and new fossil discoveries have added to our comprehension of their diversity, as have also additions to the list of described species — the list, it might be pointed out, currently includes no fewer than a million forms. Obviously, this weight of numbers alone makes the study of animal life far more complicated for the modern zoologist than it was for the Greeks. Yet the knowledge of existing creatures enables us to wander through the densest forest without fear of being attacked by a griffin or of having to answer riddles posed by a sphinx, for the information about what does exist has also to a large extent established what does not.

## II. MODERN SCHEMES OF CLASSIFICATION

While much thus is now well in hand about the extensiveness of variety among animals, not all is cut and dried by any means so far as the extent and significance of the diversification is concerned. For instance, though the figure of one million species cited above may appear quite impressive — and admittedly it is a large number — biologists generally believe that this represents perhaps only a tenth of the number of species actually extant on earth today.

Nor are the implications of kinships always clear and universally agreed upon. At the present time there is considerable disagreement in the literature over even the number of principal subdivisions into which living things appear to be arranged. Although most systematists still adhere to the concept that there are two kingdoms, one of plants, the other of animals, some suggest three or four, or even ten or more, and still others try to show that all life is one and that it is, therefore, not divisible into separate kingdoms. A brief review of these major concepts may be pertinent.

### A. The Two-Kingdom System

While this scheme of classification is often called the classical one, in the sense that it has been employed during most of biology's existence as a formal science, from a stricter standpoint this is a misnomer. As was seen above, certain Greek scholars, including Aristotle, added a third kingdom for sponges, corals, and other sessile life, and it was this scheme that persisted through much of classical and medieval times. Hence the two-kingdom scheme might be more appropriately referred to as the "neoclassical."

In any event, the content, not the name, of the system is the principal concern here. Since the major features are doubtlessly already quite familiar, the discussion need be detailed enough only to recall to mind the particulars for later comparisons. First two kingdoms are set up, one for plants, the second for animals (Fig. 1). In the Plantae are placed those forms which as a rule are immotile, usually have walls about their cells, and either manufacture their food by photosynthesis or are saprophytic.[2] This kingdom is then divided into the *Embryophyta*, which have

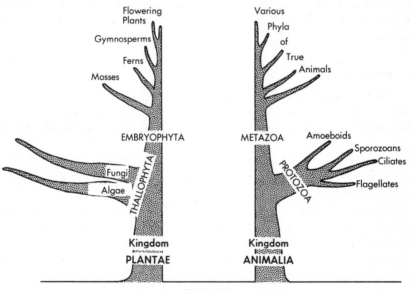

**Fig. 1.** *The two-kingdom, or classical, scheme.* This familiar system proposes separate animal and plant kingdoms that arose independently from primitive life.

an embryo during their development, and the *Thallophyta* that lack such a developmental stage. The latter is then subdivided into photosynthetic *Algae* and saprophytic *Fungi* and further arranged into divisions as shown in Table 1.

---

[2]*Saprophytic* plants are those which feed by absorbing organic substances dissolved in the surrounding medium directly into the cells. Animal-like forms that feed in a similar fashion are said to be *saprozoic*.

TABLE 1

## Comparison of Various Schemes of Classification

| Two-Kingdom | Three-Kingdom | Four-Kingdom | Single-Kingdom |
|---|---|---|---|
| I. PLANTAE | I. PROTISTA | I. MONERA (MYCHOTA) | I. PLANTAE |
| A. *Thallophyta* | 1. Green algae | 1. Bacteria and blue-green algae | A. Blue-green algae |
| 1. Green algae | 2. Yellow-green algae | II. PROTISTA (PROTOCTISTA) | B. Sulfur bacteria |
| 2. Yellow-green algae | 3. Golden-yellow algae | 1. Red algae | C. Sulfur purple bacteria |
| 3. Golden-yellow algae | 4. Diatoms | 2. Brown and yellow-green algae; diatoms, water molds | D. Slime bacteria |
| 4. Diatoms | 5. Cryptomonads | 3. Euglenoids and dinoflagellates | E. True bacteria |
| 5. Cryptomonads | 6. Dinoflagellates | 4. Chytrid fungi | F. Yeasts |
| 6. Dinoflagellates | 7. Chloromonads | 5. Fungi in part | G. Euglenoids and dinoflagellates |
| 7. Chloromonads | 8. Euglenoids | 6. Amoeboids and many flagellates | H. Thecate and soil amoeboids |
| 8. Euglenoids | 9. Blue-green algae | 7. Sporozoa | I. True amoeboids |
| 9. Blue-green algae | 10. Red algae | 8. Ciliates | J. Parasitic amoeboids |
| 10. Red algae | 11. Brown algae | III. PLANTAE | K. Protociliates |
| 11. Brown algae | 12. Ciliates | Green algae, mosses, ferns, seed plants, etc. | L. Green algae and higher green plants |
| 12. Bacteria | 13. Amoeboids not contained elsewhere | IV. ANIMALIA | M. Yellow, red, and brown algae, fungi, ciliates, sponges and metazoans |
| 13. Slime molds | 14. Flagellates not included elsewhere | Sponges and all multicellular animals | |
| 14. True fungi and yeasts | 15. Sporozoa | | |
| B. *Embryophyta* | 16. Bacteria | | |
| Mosses, ferns, seed plants, etc. | 17. True fungi and yeasts | | |
| II. ANIMALIA | II. PLANTAE | | |
| A. *Protozoa* | Mosses, ferns, seed plants, etc. | | |
| B. *Metazoa* | III. ANIMALIA | | |
| Sponges and all multicellular animals | Sponges and all multicellular animals | | |

As a rule the Animal Kingdom is divided into two subkingdoms, one for the unicellular *Protozoa*, the other for the multicellular *Metazoa*. Occasionally the sponges are removed from the latter as a separate subkingdom called the *Parazoa*, but this is exceptional to the more general treatment of that group as the most primitive phylum among the metazoans. The Protozoa formerly were divided into five classes, but this number is more frequently reduced to four. These four are the *Flagellata* or *Mastigophora*, flagellated throughout much of their life histories, the *Sarcodina*, amoeboid forms that move by pseudopods; the *Sporozoa*, parasitic species with no mean of locomotion as adults; and the *Ciliophora*, with bristles, or cilia, over their surfaces, at least in the juvenile stages. While some deviation in the terminology applied to these larger units is occasionally encountered within the animal section, many more changes have been proposed for plant subdivisions, with considerable improvement as a consequence.[3]

## B. The Multiple-Kingdom Approaches

So long as one does not delve too deeply or broadly into the unicellular forms, the foregoing scheme is quite satisfactory. Admittedly there are occasional difficulties, as, for instance, with *Euglena*, the familiar flagellated form that contains chloroplasts. Because of its active habits, zoologists class this genus as an animal among the protozoans and explain the presence of chloroplasts as indicating its relatively primitive position close to its plant forebears. To support their concept, they point to a number of other genera, including *Peranema* and *Copromonas*, which are quite similar to *Euglena* except that they, in lacking chloroplasts, are completely animal-like. At the same time botanists support their inclusion of these forms among the Algae by citing such creatures as *Colacium*. The members of this genus are, like the other genera cited, also structurally close to *Euglena* but possess chloroplasts; they are, however, usually both devoid of flagella and produce growths which are decidedly plantlike in all respects. Were these the only instances of this sort known to exist, the explanation offered by the zoologists might be acceptable, but such is far from the case. Comparable dual treatment in classification, that is, inclusion in both the Algae and the Protozoa, is encountered among many diverse types (see Table 1).

---

[3]For a more detailed discussion of the botanical aspects of this approach, reference may be made to A. Cronquist, "The Divisions and Classes of Plants." *Botanical Review*. 26:425-482, 1960. For the zoological facets, see R. E. Blackwelder, *Classification of the Animal Kingdom*, Carbondale, Ill.: Southern Illinois University Press, 1963.

To show the interrelationships more clearly among the unicellular groups, it was proposed by John Hogg in 1860 that all these organisms represent a distinct kingdom, variously called the *Protista* or *Protoctista* (Fig. 2). The kingdom *Plantae* thereby was reduced to an equivalent of the classical Embryophyta, while the the kingdom *Animalia* became equivalent to the Metazoa, including the sponges. Somewhat later, because the blue-green algae and bacteria do not possess a nucleus like that of the other protists and hence do not undergo mitosis during cell division, it was suggested by E. H. Haeckel in 1866 that these two groups likewise be removed into still another kingdom, the *Monera* (Fig. 2).

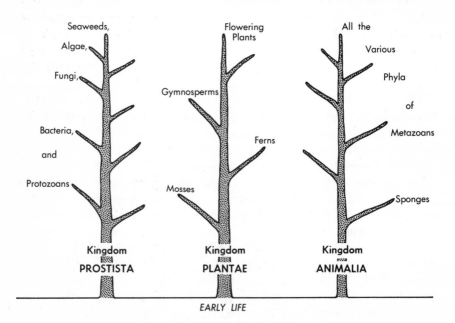

**Fig. 2.** *The three-kingdom concept.* In addition to separate plant and animal kingdoms that include the multicellular types, a third kingdom, the Protista, is included for all the algae, protozoa, and fungi.

Still greater multiplicity in kingdoms has been suggested by Smith.[4] Briefly stated, his system combines the Embryophyta and green algae as one kingdom, the euglenoids and the dinoflagellates as a second,

[4]Gilbert M. Smith, *The Fresh Water Algae of the United States,* 2nd ed., New York: McGraw-Hill Book Company, 1950. For a clear exposition of the four-kingdom concept, see J. F. Copeland, *The Classification of Lower Organisms,* Palo Alto, Calif.: Pacific Books, 1956.

called the Euglenophyta, and so on through all the algal groups. Consequently, a total of ten kingdoms is outlined. However, because this botanist was concerned solely with algae, his scheme makes no disposition for the bacteria, fungi, protozoans, and metazoans, so that, thus incomplete, it has never come into widespread use.

## C. The Single-Kingdom Concept

While the provision for more major categories avoids many of the difficulties encountered in the classical system, no relationships between the different kingdoms can be perceived when they are thus segregated from one another (Fig. 2). And it should be remembered that systematists in their schemes attempt to reflect the real kinships of organisms as closely as possible. Moreover, while the larger problems are avoided, many of the lesser ones are not; for example, the probable relationships of the chlorophyll-bearing amoeboids, the flagellated amoeboids, the ciliates, and other former Protozoa still remain unsolved.

In an attempt to overcome these shortcomings and to show relationships more clearly, a recent approach utilizes the internal structure of the

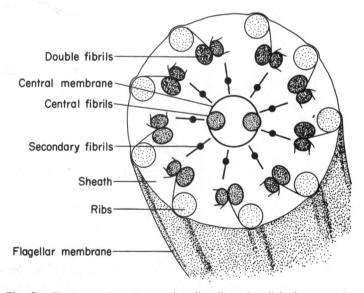

Double fibrils

Central membrane

Central fibrils

Secondary fibrils

Sheath

Ribs

Flagellar membrane

**Fig. 3.** *The internal structure of a flagellum.* In all higher organisms beginning with the euglenoids, the flagellum contains basically the same parts present in identical numbers and arranged similarly. This condition and other cell structures are employed in the single kingdom scheme to suggest sequence in evolutionary development. (Reproduced, with permission, from L. S. Dillon, *Principles of Animal Biology,* New York: The Macmillan Company, copyright 1965.)

cell and its organelles. To begin with, it makes two basic assumptions, the first being that, if life arose through biochemical means as described in the preceding chapter, the cell probably first arose in an extremely simple condition and from that point gradually became more complex. Secondly, it assumes that the living things now in existence possibly represent some of the stages in the evolution of the cell from the simple to the advanced state.

Since the structure of the nucleus has been most thoroughly studied, the tracing of what might be the cell's history is first attempted by using this organelle and its parts. Then, with the sequence of organisms thus established as a guide, the evolution of such cell parts as the flagellum (Fig. 3), mitochondrion, and chloroplast is traced, largely employing fine structural details revealed by the electron microscope. As a consequence, it is suggested that all extant organisms form a single tree of life, and hence, all belong to one kingdom. Because of the limitations of choice and for various technical reasons, this single kingdom is recognized as the Plant Kingdom, but it could with equal logic be referred to

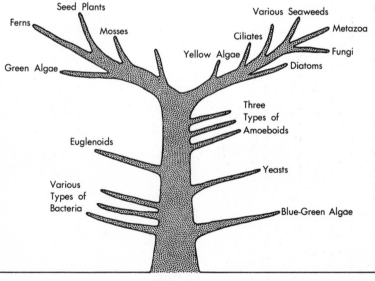

EARLY LIFE

**Fig. 4.** *The single-kingdom concept.* Based on cell structure, this scheme proposes that all things belong together in one kingdom, the major branches of which represent subkingdoms.

as the Biotic Kingdom.[5] The tree's thirteen major branches (Fig. 4) are then considered as subkingdoms, the secondary ones as phyla, and so on (Table 1). This system has a disadvantage in that a widespread upset in classification is proposed; furthermore, it is too recent to have come into general usage.

In this brief synopsis only a glimpse at the several major systems of classification can be provided; perhaps the following pages will make some of the issues clearer. Before continuing, however, the student should realize that selection of any particular scheme by a biologist is not merely a matter of opinion. Each scientist chooses the approach that best seems to fit the data with which he is familiar. In other words, classification is a matter of interpretation, not of simple preference.

----

[5]The student interested in greater detail is referred to L. S. Dillon, "Comparative Cytology and the Evolution of Life," *Evolution* 16:102-117, 1962.

# CHAPTER 3

# Diversity at the early unicellular level

The foregoing discussion makes it clear that the light microscope and, more recently, the electron microscope have disclosed much greater diversification among living things than was ever conceived previously and that these instruments have added to the complexity of the problems confronting biologists rather than simplify them. Particularly is this illustrated by the unsettled conditions pertaining to the number of kingdoms and similar broad aspects of kinships. As it is not our purpose to support any single point of view regarding these matters, the groups containing animal-like members will be treated here one by one, without any real regard for conjectural relationships. Instead, outlines of classification will be provided to indicate the several more important treatments of the groups wherever appropriate.

Before the principal types are discussed, some attention should be given to the term *protozoa*. While in the two-kingdom concept, this is, of course, employed as the name of the subkingdom that includes all unicellular animal-like forms, both the multiple-kingdom and the single-kingdom approaches alike discard it. This term, however, is too deeply ingrained in zoological literature to be cast aside entirely; moreover, it frequently can be a most convenient word to have at hand. For those using a nonclassical concept, it may be employed in a nonsystematic sense to refer to those unicellular or essentially unicellular organisms which are actively motile during much of their life histories or which parasitize any of the Metazoa. While this definition does not distinguish these organisms from the bacteria and yeasts, it still carries approximately the same implications that it has in the dual-kingdom scheme (Table 1).

Additional terms used in a systematic sense in the latter system may also be of value in the other schemes, especially those that describe the body form of the organisms. The name *flagellate*, for example, can refer in all schemes to organisms that possess one or more whiplike append- ages, or *flagella*, by means of which they move about in the water. Usually these organelles are located at the anterior end so that their movements pull the protozoans through the liquid medium, but some- times they are situated toward or upon one side, and, in rare instances, they are attached at the posterior end. In contrast, *amoeboid* organisms usually lack permanent locomotive organelles but send out and retract projections of the cytoplasm to provide movement and to assist in feed- ing. Typically such *pseudopods* are ephemeral, persisting for only a few minutes, but in some groups they are semipermanent, being retracted only under exceptional circumstances. *Ciliates* are types which possess bristle-like organelles; sometimes the *cilia* cover the greater part of the cell's surface, but in certain groups, they are confined to specialized areas. In actuality, cilia are shortened flagella, as shown in their ultra- structural details revealed by electron microscopy. *Coccoid* forms are entirely devoid of a means of locomotion and very frequently are en- closed in a wall-like covering. Quite often these organisms are spherical in shape, but they may be small crescents, elongate rods, discs, or any one of many other geometric designs.

Although agreeing with this latter variety of body form in being motionless, *palmellas* differ in having several cells enclosed in a common wall or envelope; hence, they may be viewed as being colonial coccoids. In a similar sense, a *plasmodium* (or syncytium) may be considered a colonial amoeboid type, from the usual forms of which it is distinguished in having numerous nuclei that share a common cytoplasmic mass. This simple colony is capable of sending out pseudopods as an ordinary uninu- cleate amoeba does. *Filamentous* colonies consist of long chains of threads of coccoid forms but are rarely found among animal-like groups; and, finally, *dendroid* colonies are branched filaments which are quite as scarce among protozoans as the unbranched type just mentioned.

## I. THE EUGLENOIDS

Among both botanists and zoologists it is customary to consider the flagellated body condition as the most primitive, nor will an exception to this practice be made here. Since *Euglena* and its relatives are, in turn, often suggested to be the simplest type among the flagellates, this group composes the lowermost branch of the protozoans. The many different names given to the members of this group are best enumerated in the form of a chart (Table 2).[1]

Although a number of forms are strictly marine and others live in mud banks, there can be no doubt that the chief home of these organisms is in the fresh waters of the earth. In this habitat the euglenoids frequently play a role of considerable importance, especially in ponds containing large aquatic plants or in those rich in organic matter. Sometimes they occur in such abundance that their bodies impart a characteristic color to the water. Usually green results from the presence of most species of *Euglena* or other chlorophyll-bearing types, but a brown coloration is produced by the species of *Trachelomonas* and red by *Euglena sanguinea*.

## A. Nutrition

As a whole, of course, the chlorophyll-bearing members of the group are holophytic,[2] but even though they can synthesize their own carbohydrates, they are not always entirely independent of the chemical contents of the waters in which they occur. All draw upon the dissolved minerals and, as far as is presently known, every species of *Euglena* requires at least certain amino acids present in the medium, and most forms also seem to need those short chains of amino acids referred to as peptones. To this extent all are saprozoic. In the continued absence of light, free-living *Euglena* and other normally holophytic species lose their chloroplasts and live quite well if supplied organic nutrients. Similarly treatment with the familiar antibiotic streptomycin permanently destroys the chloroplasts whether illumination is present or not; individuals treated in this fashion can nevertheless grow and multiply freely if the proper organic substances are added to the culture medium. Colorless individuals of normally chlorophyll-bearing species such as *Euglena gracilis, Phacus pleuronectes,* and *Colacium vesiculosum* can satisfy their needs for both proteins and energy sources solely from amino acids, but most forms need acetic or formic acid or simple carbohydrates in addition to a nitrogen source.

In this connection it is of interest to note that chlorophyll-less individuals sometimes develop in rapidly growing cultures of species which

---

[1]For an interesting review of the members of this group in greater detail, reference may be made to T. L. Jahn, "The Euglenoid Flagellates." *Quarterly Review of Biology.* 21:246-274, 1946.

[2]Some biologists prefer to use either "autotrophic" or "phototrophic" to designate forms that manufacture foods by photosynthesis. For a review of the nutritional habits of these organisms, see R. P. Hall, "The Trophic Nature of the Plantlike Flagellates." *Quarterly Review of Biology,* 14:1-12, 1939

TABLE 2

Names Applied to the Unicellular Groups Discussed in This Text

| Group | Two-Kingdom Scheme | | Three-Kingdom Scheme | Single-Kingdom Scheme |
|---|---|---|---|---|
| | Kingdom Plantae | Kingdom Animalia | Kingdom Protista | Kingdom Plantae |
| | *Algae* Divisions | *Protozoa* Class & Order | Phylum and Class | Subkingdom |
| Euglenoids | Euglenophyta | Flagellata : Euglenoidina | Pyrrhophyta : Mastigophora | Euglenophytaria |
| Dinoflagellates | Pyrrhophyta | Flagellata : Dinoflagellata | Pyrrhophyta : Mastigophora | Euglenophytaria |
| Amoeboids | ——— | Sarcodina : Amoebina | Protoplasta : Sarcodina | Arcellophytaria, Amoebophytaria, and Enterophytaria |
| Yellow-green protozoans | Xanthophyta | Flagellata : Chrysomonadina | Phaeophyta : Heterokontae | Chrysophytaria |
| Golden-yellow protozoans | Chrysophyta | Flagellata : Chrysomonadina | Phaeophyta : Heterokontae | Chrysophytaria |
| Green protozoans | Chlorophyta | Flagellata : Phytomonadina | Chlorophyta : several classes | Chlorophytaria |
| Trypanosomes | ——— | Flagellata : Protomonadina | Fungilli : Sporozoa | Chrysophytaria |
| Multiflagellated protozoans | ——— | Flagellata : Polymastigina, Hypermastigina | Protoplasta : Zoomastigoda | Chrysophytaria |
| True ciliates | ——— | Ciliophora : several orders | Ciliophora : Infusoria | Chrysophytaria |
| Sporozoans | ——— | Sporozoa : several orders | Fungilli : Sporozoa | Chrysophytaria |

normally possess chloroplasts. Particularly has this condition been observed in *Euglena gracilis* and *Phacus pleuronectes*. The German algologist C. Ternetz has suggested that such oddities arise when by accident the chloroplasts of a cell fail to divide during fission, for these bodies are entirely self-productive. Consequently, repeated failure of this sort results in a gradual diminution in numbers of these organelles, and, finally, a total absence in some of the descendants.

A number of the euglenoids, including the species of *Astasia* and *Distigma*, are normally colorless saprophytes, occurring in abundance in stagnant or polluted waters rich in organic matter. Other species of *Astasia* frequently are found in the intestines of vertebrates, probably as harmless commensals. Indeed this habit is not confined to colorless forms. Robert W. Hegner, the noted American protozoologist, described the occurrence of several distinct chlorophyll-bearing species of the genus *Euglena* in the cloaca of tadpoles from eastern United States. By means of a series of experiments he demonstrated that these forms cannot be cultured by ordinary means, that they will not grow in such related vertebrates as salamanders for example, and that they are accidentally passed from one individual frog to another. In other words, these species of *Euglena*, in spite of the presence of chlorophyll, can survive only within the confines of the tadpole's digestive tract, where they absorb nutrients saprozoically.

By and large most of the colorless forms are holozoic, feeding on bacteria, small algae, and protozoans. In some of these species, including members of the genera *Peranema, Entosiphon,* and *Urceolus,* a special tube or siphon is embedded within the cytoplasm toward the anterior end. This sort of structure, while movable forward and backward as well as from side to side, is really protrusible only in *Peranema* and *Entosiphon.* But, as even here its protrusibility is highly restricted, its function is not entirely clear. Possibly movement of the siphon induces a streaming action in the substrate so that suspended particles or minute organisms are caused to flow toward an opening, called the *cytostome*, which serves as a mouth.

One holozoic euglenoid, *Jenningsia*, is particularly highly specialized in food habits, for it appears to subsist on diatoms, a type of algae which is covered with a tough shell of silica. This protozoan ranks among the largest of flagellates, frequently attaining a length of 260 $\mu$. Although bearing a prominent flagellum, the organism is not known to swim, but creeps along the substrate, using its hook-ended flagellum somewhat as a paddle. When the flagellum encounters a diatom, the organism employs it as a "feeler" and moves so as to align the cytostome with one end of the intended prey. Then the anterior end of the organism expands laterally to engulf the alga, the whole process requiring perhaps twenty seconds to complete.

Regardless of the type of nutrition, all known euglenoids store excess carbohrydrates in the form of paramylum.[3] This substance is similar both to starch and to glycogen in being a complex sugar. Unlike either of these other carbohydrates, it fails to stain with iodine and is insoluble in boiling water; on the other hand it is similar to both in being soluble in potassium hydroxide and concentrated sulfuric acid. As a rule paramylum is deposited directly in the cytoplasm, not in the chloroplast as starch is in the seed plants. Deposition may be in the form of rings, rods, disks, spheres, or irregular blocks, the particular shape being constant for each species. In chlorophyll-bearing types, the size and number of paramylum grains increase rapidly during active photosynthesis and decrease during starvation, so the employment of these particles as food reserves appears evident.

## B. Cell Characteristics

While here and elsewhere throughout this book structural details are presented mainly in the illustrations, certain features of the cell among the euglenoids are so unique that they require at least a brief discussion in addition to the figure (Fig. 5).

### Structural Details

It has not always been realized that *Euglena* and others which appear to have only one flagellum actually have two; the second one in these forms, being embedded in the cell covering (the *pellicle*), is not visible unless special techniques are used. Under the electron microscope each flagellum can be seen to bear hairlike structures called *flimmer*. In the present protozoans the flimmer are confined to a single row on one side of the flagellum, whereas in other groups when present, they are arranged in two rows except in the dinoflagellates.

The short canal at the anterior end has as often as not been labeled the gullet, pharynx, or similar term suggestive of an ingestive function. But it has been shown by Hall and other workers that in those forms which engulf prey, as has already been pointed out, a special opening (the *cytostome*) is present, which is in no way associated with this canal. Since the contractile vacuoles empty their contents into the canal

---

[3]Often referred to also as paramylon.

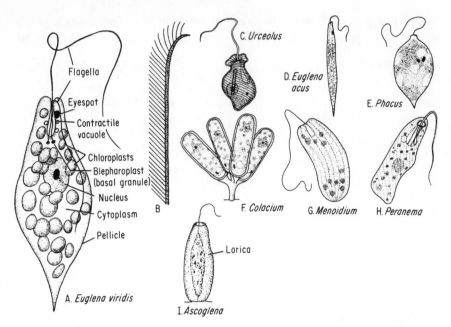

**Fig. 5.** *Euglenoid structure and types. A.* The principal structural features of euglenoids. *B.* The tip of a flagellum with flimmer confined to one side. *C-I.* Various representatives of the euglenoids proper. Rarely simple colonies occur, like those of *Colacium (F).* (Reproduced, with permission, from L. S. Dillon, *The Science of Life,* New York: The Macmillan Company, copyright 1964.)

its only likely function is that of carrying off excreted water and other waste products. Hence, the less commonly employed name *excretory canal* seems more appropriate for this organelle.

Some of the most characteristic features of euglenoid cytology become evident only during cell division. Within the centrally placed nucleus is a body of chromatin called the *endosome.* When the nucleus undergoes mitosis, the endosome elongates until it finally splits into two approximately equal parts. In the meantime chromosomes appear and behave quite normally; however, no spindle fibers or interzonal lines can be noted during the mitotic processes. Hence, the nucleus is seen to consist solely of a nuclear membrane, nucleoplasm, chromosomes, and the endosome, which some workers consider a primitive nucleolus. It is because of the relative simplicity of the nucleus that the euglenoids are frequently treated as the most primitive of the animal-like unicellular organisms. The chloroplasts and mitochondria also are rather simple in construction.

## C. Behavior

Because behavior is basically comparable in all flagellates, that of the euglenoids can serve as the example for the rest, no matter what their relationships. Consequently detailed attention to this aspect can be given here.

Behavior patterns in the euglenoids, as in other flagellates, are based primarily upon changes in the method of swimming under the influence of various stimuli. Normally the path followed when swimming is in the form of a narrow spiral. Because the cell rotates on its longitudinal axis once with each complete spiral twist, a certain side of the organism always faces the spiral's outside. As a matter of convenience, this special side is referred to as the *dorsal surface*.

### Reaction to Contact and Chemicals

When a freely swimming euglenoid encounters a solid object, it reverses its movement briefly, then resumes a forward motion. However, the spiral course is now widened so that the anterior end points successively in many directions, in any one of which the organism may finally swim forward. If, after forward movement is resumed, the obstacle is again encountered, the protozoan repeats the whole performance, reversing its direction, swerving widely in a broad spiral, and then swimming forward again. When large obstructions are involved, this *avoidance behavior* pattern may be repeated many times before a clear path is found.

In the case of a mild chemical stimulus, such as the presence of a dilute acid in the medium, the reaction is similar, but with a few slight differences. When the chemical initially is encountered, the organism, instead of abruptly reversing, first retards its forward movement and then stops swimming momentarily. Frequently no reversal may occur before a wide spiral path is assumed. This broadened pattern may be continued for some distance until a more favorable region is reached, when normal swimming begins once more. If a more intense chemical stimulus is encountered, the euglenoid may contract into a sphere, retract its flagella, and secrete a protective coat about itself and thus *encyst*.

Among many of the euglenoids, including *Peranema*, an entirely different type of reaction may be shown on encountering a solid object. The members of the genus mentioned, although quite capable of swimming, frequently react to contact with solid surfaces by creeping upon them. In creeping, the cell is repeatedly looped and straightened in a strikingly wormlike fashion. Most species of *Euglena*, too, can progress in like manner — in fact this type of locomotion was first observed in this genus and is named "euglenoid" movement accordingly. Some genera carrying this habit even further. As discussed earlier, *Jenningsia*, the diatom-eating euglenoid, has not been observed to swim in spite of its well-developed flagellum, but creeps about the substrate in a peculiar fashion.

### Reaction to Light

As might be anticipated, the pigmented euglenoids react differently to light than the so-called colorless members of the group, but, as the distinction is merely one of direction, only the former type needs to be described in detail. If several drops of medium containing *Euglena* are placed on a microscope slide and observed under a stereoscopic microscope near a window, most of the organisms may soon be seen swimming toward the light. If the light now is screened by means of the hand or other device, the flagellates immediately display the avoidance reaction, reversing their direction of movement or at least ceasing to swim. This initial response is then followed in turn by the wide spiral pattern described above and a resumption of forward progress in a new direction.

The first reaction to diminished light intensity is a very striking one, for all the organisms respond nearly simultaneously, even those individuals that may have by chance been swimming away from the window when the culture was shaded. Hence it is clear that the response is produced by the change in intensity, not by a change in direction of the light. This interpretation is further substantiated by the euglenoids' resuming their original direction even when the illumination is maintained in the decreased state for several moments.

By throwing shadows on individual portions of the organism, Engelmann established in 1882 that shading only the extreme anterior tip was just as effective as decreasing the light on the entire organism. Through use of similar procedures it has been shown that the eye-spot in *Euglena* is not light-sensitive at all and that the base of the flagellum is the actual light-receptor organ; the eye-spot, or stigma, merely acts as a shield. Orientation toward a light source results from a series of avoidance reactions, during each set of which the swerving sequence occurs when the shadow of the stigma falls across the flagellar base (Fig. 6). Only after the anterior end of the organism has become approximately aligned with the direction of the light rays so that the flagellar base is constantly illuminated does the spiral course of swimming narrow to its normal condition.

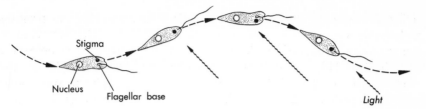

**Fig. 6.** *Movement in Euglena in response to light.* The eyespot in *Euglena* is not sensitive to light but partially shields the light-receptor organ, the flagellar base. Orientation toward light is brought about by a series of avoidance reactions.

While chlorophyll-bearing forms are thus *positively phototropic* — that is, they react to light by moving toward the source — if the light becomes too intense their reaction is in the opposite direction. Those forms that do not contain chlorophyll are likewise negatively phototropic, no matter how dim the light. In other words, even a small amount of light is "too much" as it were; hence, in many of the colorless species, the stigma may be absent.

Among some of the chlorophyllous euglenoids a bright red pigment is often present in the cytoplasm that responds to changes in light intensity as well as to temperature. This pigment, called haematochrome, is found particularly in *Euglena sanguinea* and *E. rubra;* its behavior has been most thoroughly explored in the latter species, especially by Drs. L. P. Johnson and T. L. Jahn. The first of these protozoologists[4] found that in sunlit pools this organism is red during the day but becomes dull green toward sunset. The color change comes about as a consequence of a movement of the pigment within the cell. When the haematochrome is concentrated within the interior of the cytoplasm, the color of the peripherally located chloroplasts predominates, so that the organism is green. On the other hand, when the free pigment migrates to the periphery, the chlorophyll is concealed, so that the *Euglena* appears bright red. If a portion of the pond is shaded with a screen early in the morning, the water later becomes colored bright red except in the shaded area; when the screen is removed, however, the red coloration develops there too, requiring about eleven minutes for completion of the change. Still later in the day the pond resumes a uniform green coloring. Similar changes from green to red have been found to be produced by an increase in the water's temperature to higher than 30° C. It is sug-

---

[4] See L. P. Johnson, "A Study of *Euglena rubra* Hardy," *Transactions of the American Microscopial Society,* 58:42-48, 1939.

gested that the role of the haematochrome may be protective, shielding the chloroplasts from too intense sun or heat but retreating so as to expose the chloroplasts under more favorable conditions. At any rate both *E. rubra* and *E. sanguinea* appear capable of growing under warmer conditions than most of their relatives.

## II. THE DINOFLAGELLATES

In marked contrast to the euglenoids, in which conformity to a common pattern of structure is the rule, the dinoflagellates exhibit wide diversification. The variation among the species is so extensive that, were intermediate forms not extant, it would be difficult to perceive any relationship between the primitive and highly specialized species. Also unlike the euglenoids, the dinoflagellates are largely marine, although they do inhabit fresh waters to some extent. However, far greater morphological diversity is found among the salt-water members. In the seas specialization in relation to temperature is a striking feature, some groups being confined to warm waters and others to the cooler regions. Moreover adaptation exists in relation to depths, those without a heavy cell wall, or armor, being found in the open waters over the deeps, whereas the armored kinds abound in shallower waters close to shore. Some species even inhabit the shores themselves; members of such genera as *Amphidinium* and *Gymnodinium* at certain seasons of the year grow so abundantly as to color the sand greenish brown.

### Cell Characteristics

Because of the high degree of diversity mentioned above, it is virtually impossible to define the group on the basis of the external characteristics of its components; however, it is possible, as is shown later, to find traits within the nucleus that are common to all its members. But first the organisms themselves need to be described.

### *Diversity of Structure*

Undoubtedly the least specialized dinoflagellates are those naked unicellular species known collectively as *desmomonads,* a type scarcely distinguishable superficially from the euglenoids in general structure. On the obliquely cut anterior end are two flagella, while inside are usually many chloroplasts; in a few genera, however, such as *Haplodinium,* there is a single large one (Fig. 7). Within the cells, too, is found the beginning of one trait that is characteristic of this entire group —

the presence of vacuoles. Furthermore, starch of a peculiar sort, in contrast to *Euglena's* paramylum, is deposited as a food reserve. If a living specimen is examined, the earliest stages of a later marked peculiarity of the flagella can be perceived. Although one flagellum vibrates in the usual fashion, the second one projects horizontally, often beating in a circular fashion rather than with typical whiplike movements (Fig. 7).

All these features are found in much the same state also among the *prorocentrads,* but these organisms show one advancement toward the more specialized stock. This added feature is the *theca,* or coat, that is so strikingly developed later; here, however, the theca is simply a thin coat or cell wall, perforated by numerous pores and made of two separate halves joined by longitudinal sutures (Fig. 7). A pore in the coat permits the two flagella to protrude.

In the *dinophysids,* the same divided theca is found along with the beginnings of the most characteristic features of the definitive members.

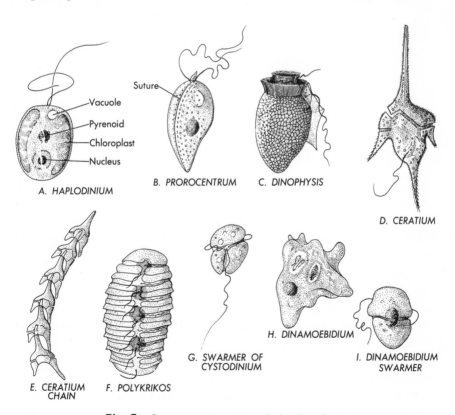

**Fig. 7.** *Representative types of dinoflagellates.*

The pore through which the flagella emerge has migrated somewhat toward one side, and the flagellum that formerly projected anteriorly to pull the organism along now points in the opposite direction so that it provides a pushing action. In its new lateral position, the second flagellum still is directed horizontally but it coils now enclose the organism. As shown in *Dinophysis* the theca is provided with two deep grooves which receive both flagella (Fig. 7).

Among the most highly developed members of the group, the *armored dinoflagellates*, these traits are only slightly modified. The chief change from the dinophysid condition is in the relocation of the transverse groove and the flagellum it encloses, which is here situated more posteriorly near the middle of the cell, as shown in *Ceratium* (Fig. 7). As suggested by the common name of this section, the theca in these forms is so thickened as to be referred to as armor and is subdivided into several plates, with long spines of frequent occurrence. Sometimes as in *Ceratium tripos*, the products of division remain attached to form long filamentous colonies. In *Polykrikos* a colonial condition also is found, but in this genus the theca of each new individual is completely continuous with that of an older one. Moreover, the cytoplasm is not subdivided into discrete cells, so that the organism is a plasmodium, with a continuous cytoplasmic mass enclosing a number of nuclei. Still other members of the dinoflagellates proper are coccoids, the flagella being lost in the adult; only the reproductive cells, called *swarmers* or *zoospores*, are motile, as in *Cystodinium* (Fig. 7). Certain of these coccoid forms, for instance *Blastodinium*, are parasitic in various crustaceans and segmented worms.

However, the sequence of developments presented above outlines the changes along only one major branch. Other lines of specialization exist, too, but space limitations restrict discussion to brief mention of one particularly pertinent type. This variety, represented by *Dinamoebidium*, is a large amoeba-like organism that lacks both flagella and chloroplasts; normally it lives on the sea bottom, creeping about by means of short pseudopods. Under the proper conditions it encysts and then undergoes mitotic division to produce four to eight swarmers. These reproductive cells alone show the grooves, flagella, and other characteristic features of the group.

### Internal Traits

To date few detailed studies into the fine structure of the dinoflagellates have been conducted, so relatively little is known of the ultrastructure of the cell organelles. As a whole the nucleus resembles that of the euglenoids in lacking interzonal lines and spindle threads. A further similarity to that group is found in the presence of a large endosome in the simpler members, but this characteristic is gradually lost in successively higher representatives. The flagella, too, are of like internal construction (Fig. 3) but externally the trailing member differs in being devoid of flimmer. However, the encircling flagellum possesses a single row of flimmer, as in the euglenoids, despite its being extensively buried in the body covering. It is because of these similarities in unique traits that the dinoflagellates and euglenoids are frequently considered to be closely related.

## III. THE AMOEBOIDS

Among the various predominantly flagellated groups are scattered representatives which move by means of pseudopods and which are therefore amoeboids in every sense of that term. Yet in each case those amobae possess other cellular features that very clearly indicate their relationships to the flagellated taxon in question. One such instance, *Dinamoebidium*, has already been described, and others will be encountered later. However, there are numerous colorless species which do not share characteristics with any other group but have in common many distinctive traits in addition to an amoeboid type of movement. It is these organisms that will receive attention at this time. Since these amoeboids can serve as the illustration for the other unicellular forms which move by the same means, locomotion and behavior patterns can be described in more detail than might otherwise be warranted.

### A. Locomotion

While several types of locomotion occur among amoeboids, all can be arranged into three principal categories. First is the common pseudopodal variety in which one or more variously shaped pseudopods are projected outward. This action is followed by a flowing movement on the part of the remaining cytoplasm, accompanied by marked changes in cell shape. To the contrary, both the second and the third type are characterized by a high degree of stability in cell form. The second, called the *limax* type after a species of *Vahlkampfia* by that name, moves as a single unit, usually a more or less oblong, elongated mass (Fig. 8). Because of the relatively rapid movement and the transparent, seemingly fluid cytoplasm, a limax amoeba closely resembles a flowing droplet of water or, perhaps better, a moving garden slug. The third and final type moves more deliberately than the last, the cytoplasm appears much less fluid, and the surface of the cell is greatly wrinkled. Probably the most familiar representative is *Thecamoeba verrucosa*.

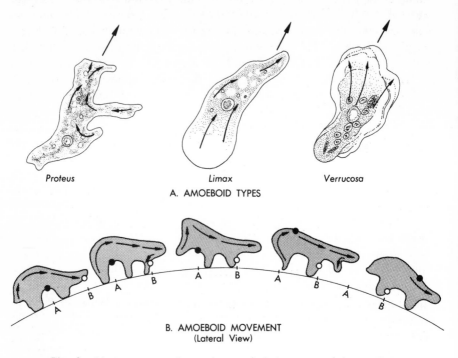

*Proteus*  *Limax*  *Verrucosa*

A. AMOEBOID TYPES

B. AMOEBOID MOVEMENT
(Lateral View)

**Fig. 8.** *Various types of amoebae and their means of locomotion.*

Regardless of type, the forward progress of an amoeba can best be likened to the tread of a military tank or so-called caterpillar tractor. When viewed from the side in other words, the upper surface of a moving amoeba is seen to flow forward, descend upon attaining the anteriormost point, and then remain stationary when it contacts the surface of the substrate. Only after the remainder of the cell has progressed completely over a given point does that part ascend to the upper surface to flow forward once more. In profile the front edge of an actively moving amoeboid appears thin and rather flat, while the posterior portion is high and rounded. Moreover, on closer scrutiny, the entire lower portion may be observed to be free of the substrate, supported by several short vertically placed pseudopods (Fig. 8).

As seen from the side, then, movement in amoeboids is far more complex than is evident from above. As Bell and Jeon point out,[5] no theory advanced to date accounts for the formation of pseudopods in a completely satisfactory manner. All take into consideration the establishment of only a single pseudopod, whereas several are usually produced concurrently, and none explains the rolling movement of the cytoplasmic membrane.

## B. Behavior

### Reaction to Stimuli

When an amoeba encounters a broad solid object, forward movement ceases, then after a pause, a new pseudopod is sent out near the posterior end. Complete reversal of direction is not usually attained, however, as the new pseudopod develops slightly to one side of the tail region; consequently the new course that is pursued lies at an obtuse angle to the original one (Fig. 9).

While accordingly amoeboids appear to react negatively to contact, there is another aspect that needs consideration. When an amoeba becomes suspended in water, the organism, being entirely free of contact with anything solid, is as completely unstimulated by mechanical stimuli as is possible. Since it cannot then move from place to place or feed, this situation is not a favorable one for the amoeba, and it reacts by sending out long pseudopods in all directions, reducing the cell proper to a small central axis of the projections (Fig. 9). Thus outstretched, these organ-

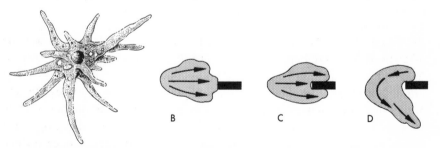

A. AMOEBA FLOATING          B-D. AMOEBA AVOIDING AN OBJECT

**Fig. 9.** *Response of amoebae to a solid object and to suspension in water.*

---

[5]L. G. E. Bell, and K. W. Jeon. "Locomotion of *Amoeba proteus,*" *Nature* 198:675-676, 1963.

elles have a much greater opportunity of encountering a solid object. As soon as one pseudopod happens to do so, it spreads out and clings to the surface. Then by means of streaming activities throughout the cytoplasm, the other pseudopods shorten and the organism eventually flows onto the surface of the contacted object to resume normal behavior.

### Reaction to Food.

One of the common foods of amoebae consists of the spherical cysts of *Euglena,* but because of their smooth surface, they roll readily and frequently present considerable difficulty to an amoeba attempting to engulf them. When an amoeba encounters a cyst that rolls away as soon as contacted, it approaches the object again. To be successful in this second attempt, upon approaching close to the encysted euglenoid the amoeba first halts the forward movement of that portion of its cell directly in line with the cyst. Then a pseudopod is formed on each side of the food, while simultaneously a thin sheet of cytoplasm is sent over the top. After passing the cyst's middle the two pseudopodal tips approach one another and finally fuse along with the overlying cytoplasmic sheet. In this manner the cyst becomes completely enclosed, together with a quantity of water, to form a so-called food vacuole.

Besides euglenoids, amoebae prey on a variety of other microorganisms — paramecia, algae, and even one another. One case of attempted cannibalism recorded by Jennings in 1903 clearly shows that the feeding reaction of these organisms is not always so simple as may appear. This noted protozoologist had attempted to cut an amoeba in two but succeeded only in incompletely separating the posterior third, which still clung to the main portion by a slender thread of cytoplasmic membrane. The anterior part, hereafter called Amoeba A, began to move away, with the remnant, to be known as Amoeba B, dragging along behind it. Amoeba B had assumed the form of a ball when Amoeba C, which was quite a large specimen, approached from one side. By accident in passing, B came briefly into contact with C, which immediately turned and began to engulf it. However, just as pseudopods had nearly surrounded B, Amoeba A turned into a new path, so that C lost the intended food momentarily. Upon pursuing the prey further, the larger specimen finally was able to enclose B firmly within its cytoplasm, whereupon the cord attaching the prey to Amoeba A broke. After being nearly completely surrounded by its captor's cytoplasm, B, which up to this point had remained a passive sphere, suddenly became active and sent pseudopods through the rapidly narrowing channel that still existed to the outside.

In this manner it nearly escaped, only to be attacked again and this time completely engulfed. Through C's movements, B soon found itself close to the posterior edge of that amoeba and, by sending out pseudopods actively, liberated itself once more. After a repetition of the whole performance — pursuit, engulfing, and subsequent escape — Amoebe C no longer pursued B but went off in another direction.

# CHAPTER 4

# Diversification of more advanced unicellular forms

As the three preceding groups illustrate the major features of structure and behavior found among the unicellular organisms, the remainder do not need to be presented in such detail. Though treated relatively briefly, the present ones should not be considered as of less importance by any means; on the contrary, several of the groups discussed here are of particular biological value. Moreover, they serve to make clear the variety of specialization that becomes possible as better cellular organization is achieved. Nor should the sequence employed be thought to suggest relationships. For the various proposals made concerning kinships, reference can be made to Table 2; here the arrangement serves other purposes.

## I. THE YELLOW FLAGELLATES AND THEIR RELATIVES

In most zoology textbooks, the yellow flagellates and their kin receive little attention, so the two taxa now under consideration are relatively unfamiliar. Yet both members form essential units in an account involving biological parallelisms that follows shortly.

The two groups referred to are the yellow-green and the golden-yellow protozoans (see Table 2 for technical names). Although differing somewhat in pigmentation, they have in common many traits which are highly distinctive, so that a combined approach to their study offers the advantage of some simplification. Shared characteristics are found primarily in the form and location of the flagella. These organelles, instead of being situated at the extreme anterior end, are placed slightly laterally on the cell, with one of the pair extended anteriorly, the other posteriorly. Moreover, the anterior flagellum has two rows of flimmer, whereas the other is completely bare; both have the tip stretched out into a slender whiplash (Fig. 10).

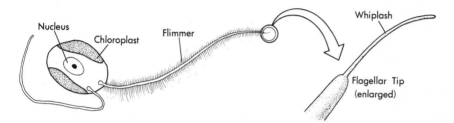

**Fig. 10.** *Cellular properties of yellow flagellates.*

A second set of unique features is provided by the absence of starch and the deposition of oil or fat as the end product of metabolism, while the third set of traits held in common is found in the pigmentation. In each group the chloroplast contains chlorophylls *a* and *c*, but the green color of those compounds is concealed to a greater or lesser extent by yellow pigments called xanthophylls. A smaller quantity of the xanthophylls accounts for the characteristic color of the chloroplast indicated by the name of the yellow-green protozoans and a higher concentration for the bright orange organelle of the golden-yellow variety.

### A. The Yellow-Green Protozoans

Probably the chief contribution of this relatively scarce group, the yellow-green protozoans, is in indicating the greater variety of body organization that is possible once the cell has advanced to a relatively high level of development. While the simplest type represented here is the flagellated, exemplified by *Chlorochromonas* (Fig. 11), it shows nothing of especial note, aside from the distinctive features of the whole group. However, a second simple variety is quite striking in accentuating the difficulties of classifying types objectively. Among its representative genera, several like *Chloramoeba* and *Heterochloris* are flagellated under certain conditions but amoeboid under others; *Heterochloris* goes so far as to lose its flagella completely at times and forms long fillamentous pseudopods (Fig. 11). Another genus, *Stipitococcus*, carries the development still a little further. Its members are amoeboid during most of their

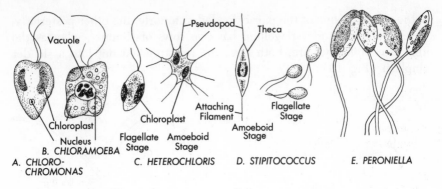

**Fig. 11.** *Diversity among yellow-green protozoans.*

lives and inhabit open vaselike thecae (Fig. 11); after cell division, however, one daughter cell acquires flagella and leaves its original theca. These organelles persist only until the organism finds a favorable location; then after attaching to the substrate by a fine filament and enclosing itself in a theca, the organism resumes the amoeboid condition. Consequently, in the classical system of classification, difficulty is experienced in deciding whether a given genus should be considered a member of the Flagellata or of the Sarcodina.

While many other genera of this group are coccoid, most of those types are customarily treated as algae. A few, however, are considered to be protozoan, including one whose members secrete a stalked theca similar to those of *Stipitococcus*. This form, called *Peroniella*, has rather stout organs of attachment and protective coverings which are entirely closed; as in the genus already mentioned flagellated swarmers are also employed here in reproduction. A final type, consisting of long filamentous colonies in which the individual cells are variously coccoid or amoeboid, is also of frequent occurrence. Although usually considered algal, the flagellated swarmers of this variety nevertheless show all the characteristic features of the protozoans assigned to the yellow-green group.

### B. The Golden-Yellow Protozoans

Except for the names of the representatives, what has been outlined above for the yellow-green protozoans could be repeated word for word here for the golden-yellow forms. Free-swimming flagellates are well represented; indeed, until relatively recent times the group was believed to consist solely of flagellated species. Possibly the most familiar examples of this type belong to the genera *Ochromonas* and *Chromulina*

(Fig. 12). Among certain other representatives diversification is exhibited by the deposition about the cell of a vaselike theca, as in *Derepyxis*, or of a covering of thick scales (e.g. *Mallomonas*).

Although the flagellum-bearing sorts are the most common, amoeboid forms are far from scarce. In fact Dr. Libbie Hyman,[1] one of the foremost specialists in invertebrates, says: "The whole order exhibits strong

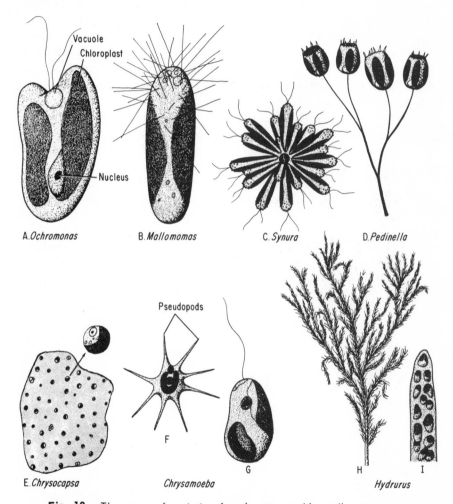

**Fig. 12.** *The range of variation found among golden-yellow protozoa.* Unicellular types (*A, B, G*), spherical colonies (*C*), stalked colonies (*D*), plasmodia (*E*), amoeboids (*F*), and complex dendroid colonies (*H*) are represented within this group. (Reproduced, with permission, from L. S. Dillon, *The Science of Life*, New York: The Macmillan Company, copyright 1964.)

39

amoeboid tendencies and shows affinities in many directions. Thus they may pass into the palmella stage and resemble algae; or lose the chloroplasts and appear as protomonads [a simple group of animal-like flagellates]; or by loss of both flagella and chloroplasts become indistinguishable from typical rhizopods [amoeboids]." At least one genus, *Chrysamoeba*, is transitional in being either flagellated or amoeboid with equal facility, while the extremity of the amoeboid condition is represented by *Rhizochrysis*, which contains chloroplasts but is not known to form flagella at any time — even the reproductive bodies are amoeboid.

Colonial representatives also are highly diversified and include one type that has not been encountered among any of the groups described so far. This variety consists of a number of flagellated cells arranged as a sphere that floats about in the water. Although not infrequently the spheres are made entirely of naked flagellates, as in *Synura* and *Skadovskiella*, many genera like *Syncrypta* are enclosed in a gelatinous envelope. Occasional members of the latter variety are equipped with long rods or needles, which, as in *Chrysosphaerella*, may be freely movable.

Another colony of common occurrence within this group is the dendroid type. Most of the representatives, including *Pedinella* and *Dendromonas*, are quite simple in consisting of only three or four flagellated individuals; the cells are pigmented in the first-named genus and chlorophyll-less in the second. Other colonies are formed of series of flagellates enveloped in open capsules, frequently with that of one individual attached directly to another, as shown in *Stylobryon* and *Dinobryon* (Fig. 13). Perhaps the most striking dendroid variety is *Uroglena*. While

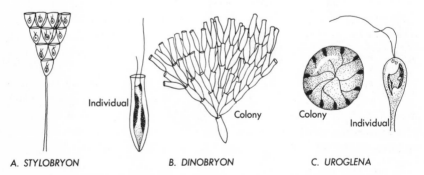

**Fig. 13.** *Other representative types of the golden-yellow protozoa.*

[1]Libbie H. Hyman. *The Invertebrates: Protozoa through Ctenophora*, New York: McGraw-Hill Book Company, 1940, p. 90.

this colony is constructed like *Chrysodendron,* it is entirely embedded in a gelatinous coat and floats in the water, so that it bears a close resemblance to the spherical colonies described above (Fig. 12).

Palmelloid colonies are also highly developed, in some genera (e.g., *Phaeosphaera* and *Hydrurus*) consisting of branched growths up to 15 inches in height. In these, hundreds of coccoid individuals are loosely arranged in a gelatinous matrix. *Hydrurus* (Fig. 12) forms especially complex colonies in cold fresh-water streams that are indistinguishable, insofar as construction is concerned, from forms uniformly considered to be algae. Yet most protozoologists list this genus among the protozoans.

## II. GREEN FLAGELLATES AND RELATED FORMS

Probably the most sharply defined of the chlorophyll-bearing protozoan groups is that now to be discussed. Among its distinctive features is the formation of starch as the storage product of metabolism, a substance formed even in those which lack chloroplastids. Where present the latter organelle usually is a single large, cup-shaped body, filling much of the posterior half of the organism and enclosing the nucleus. Besides the chlorophyll *a* found in almost all pigmented, single-celled organisms, a second type, chlorophyll *b,* is also present. As the chlorophylls are more abundant than the xanthophylls, the chloroplastids are bright green in color.

Another characteristic feature is a cellulose cell wall; although often well developed, in the simpler representatives it is sometimes completely absent. The flagella also are distinctive. With the exception of a few of the most primitive flagellated members, these organelles are devoid of flimmer; the tips are always simply rounded and lack the prolonged whiplash characteristic of the yellow-flagellated protozoans. Also with the exception of the lower members, centrioles are either lacking or degenerate.

These and other distinctions are shown diagrammatically in Figure 14. Because this highly unique combination of traits is shared with the mosses, ferns and allies, and seed plants, the green unicellular forms are generally considered ancestral to those higher plants, even to the point of being included within the same taxon in some outlines of classification.

*The Colonial Forms.*

Probably the principal contribution of the group is provided by the body types showing a high degree of parallelism with the two taxa of yellow flagellates just described. As in those protozoans the series commences with solitary flagellates, *Chlamydomonas* being the most noted representative. Coccoid species also are abundant, and these in turn lead to loose colonies of four to eight cells held together in open circles by delicate strands of cytoplasm (see *Dangeradinella*, Fig. 14).

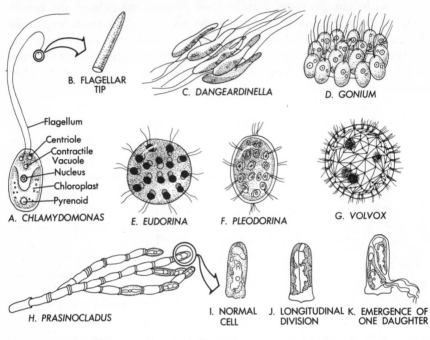

**Fig. 14.** *Structure and diversity in green protozoa.*

Following this circular type are numbers of spherical floating colonies. The sequence begins as a flat cluster of flagellated individuals embedded in a gelatinous matrix, as shown by *Gonium* (Fig. 14), while in slightly more advanced genera the cells are scattered around the matrix's periphery to form more or less perfect spheres as in *Eudorina*. At a still higher level, represented by *Pleodorina* (Fig. 14), the cells are both more numerous and more evenly spaced, while at the height of development exemplified by *Volvox*, the colonies may consist of more than 20,000 cells, all interconnected by cytoplasmic threads.

All spherical colonies are considered to be *polarized*, for they always swim with one region forward. This region, the so-called anterior end, is further specialized in *Volvox* and *Pleodorina* for strictly vegetative functions. There the cells are smaller in size, have larger stigmata, and are incapable of reproduction. In contrast, the components at the posterior end are specialized primarily for propagative activities. Among these posterior cells asexual processes continue more or less constantly throughout life, the daughter cells either remaining to increase the size of the parent colony or breaking off in clusters to form miniature colonies of their own. As the latter usually develop within the cavity of the large sphere, they escape when mature to the exterior through ruptures in the wall of the parent. At certain times sexual reproduction also occurs; some of the posterior cells enlarge to form eggs while others undergo multiple fission to establish clusters of flagellated sperm. Although most species of *Volvox* are bisexual, in a few the male and female gametes are produced in separate colonies.

Palmelloid colonies very similar in morphology to those of such yellow flagellates as *Hydrurus* and *Phaerosphaera* are both well developed and of frequent occurrence; however, these, as well as filamentous colonial species, are in the present group usually considered to be algae. Hence consideration will be given to only one of these, a genus namd *Prasinocladus*, which makes it particularly clear the difficulties involved in even distinguishing sharply between each seemingly distinct types as flagellates and filamentous colonies. In this marine organism the cells are held in chainlike series largely by the cell wall as in most filamentous algae, but cell division occurs longitudinally, not transversely. After division the daughter cells move so as to occupy upper and lower positions; the lower one thereafter remains in the parental chamber, while the upper one secretes new cell walls and thus extends the filament. Periodically the apical cell may add to the filament without undergoing division. On such occasions the cell develops four flagella and uses these to assist in migrating upward as it secretes a new set of walls. In similar fashion any cell in the filament may also develop flagella, break free, and eventually establish a new colony (Fig. 14).

## III. OTHER ANIMAL-LIKE FORMS

While it becomes apparent from the foregoing discussion that certain pigmented flagellates and amoeboids have added greatly to the zoologist's problem of discerning marked differences between protozoans and algae, and hence, between animals and plants, the remaining groups offer no such difficulty. All those that follow are obviously animal-like in habit and appear to have no close relatives among plantlike groups.

## A. The Trypanosomes

The important assemblage of the trypanosomes contains a large number of forms which are parasitic in vertebrates, including man and his domestic animals. Within the cell is a large granule called the basal body or blepharoplast, which is closely associated with the base of the flagellum; as only one or two other unicellular types are known to possess a similar organelle, this provides a ready means for identifying the members of the present taxon.

### Principal Types

Among the trypanosomes four principal types occur, which differ primarily in flagellar characteristics. The first, *Leishmania,* is normally coccoid, with the blepharoplast placed some distance anterior to the nucleus (Fig. 15). To this form the second (*Leptomonas*) is similar except that a single flagellum is present at the anterior end. In the third variety of basal body is located close to the nucleus, so that the flagellum arises near the middle of one side; from that point this organelle extends anteriorly, embedded in the plasma membrane in such a fashion that a thin flap is produced. This extension, known as the undulating membrane, is employed in swimming. In the fourth variety, *Trypanosoma,* the basal body and the flagellum's point of origin have migrated to the posterior portion of the organism, so that the undulating membrane now occupies one entire side of the cell.

As indicated before, many of these forms are important parasites, largely in the blood of vertebrates. For example, *Leishmania donovani* is the causative agent of *Kala-azar,* a disease of mankind found in the northern half of Africa and in southern Asia. Primarily this parasite invades the white blood cells and the organs that form such cells, including

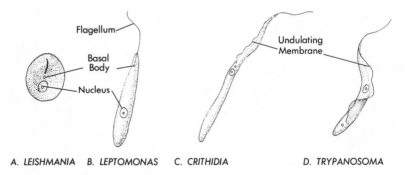

A. *LEISHMANIA*   B. *LEPTOMONAS*   C. *CRITHIDIA*   D. *TRYPANOSOMA*

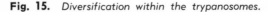

**Fig. 15.** *Diversification within the trypanosomes.*

the spleen, bone marrow, and lymph glands, as well as the liver. It appears to be transmitted from one individual to another by a biting fly of the genus *Phlebotamus,* in which it lives in a *Leptomonas*-like stage.

The principal parasitic species, however, belong to the genus *Trypanosoma,* which as a whole live free in the blood stream. Like all the pathogenic members of the genus, the two in Africa that affect man are strictly tropical in distribution. These two, *T. gambiense* and *T. rhodesiense,* are the causative organisms of African sleeping sickness and are transmitted by tsetse flies belonging to the genus *Glossina.* After spending a period in the human blood stream, the pathogens enter the nervous system and produce a lethargic condition and later death.

### B. Multiflagellated Types

Among certain protozoans usually considered to constitute two orders, multiplicity of flagella is a conspicuous feature. Although several forms have as few as four of these organelles, others possess six, eight, or upwards to several hundred. In *Trichomonas* and its kin two distinctive organelles are found at the flagellar base, including a large parabasal body. In addition there is an elongate rodlike organelle called the *axostyle,* the function of which is unknown. The majority of the species appear to feed on bacteria and yeasts within the intestines of vertebrates; however, a few species occur in the internal organs of termites and leeches.

The greatest number of flagella occurs among these protozoans that inhabit the intestines of termites and wood roaches (Fig. 16). Although these insects feed solely on wood, the enzymes necessary to digest that material appear to be absent; consequently, if treated with an antibiotic

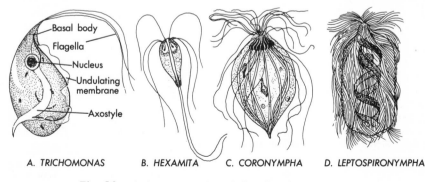

A. TRICHOMONAS    B. HEXAMITA    C. CORONYMPHA    D. LEPTOSPIRONYMPHA

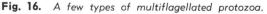

**Fig. 16.** *A few types of multiflagellated protozoa.*

that kills their normal protozoan inhabitants, the insects, despite their continuing to feed upon wood as usual, soon die of starvation. In turn, the protozoans are unable to survive outside the digestive tract of their hosts. This interdependency for existence is one of the most striking cases known to biology of a mutually beneficial association between different species of organisms.

### C. The True Ciliates[2]

A highly adaptive group, the ciliates occupy a large variety of habitats that includes fresh and marine waters as well as the internal organs of multicellular animals. Most of them swim actively by means of shortened flagella called *cilia*, which coat much of their body surface; others, however, possess fused tufts of cilia, known as *cirri*, by means of which they creep about pond and sea bottoms (Fig. 17).

All true ciliates are at once distinguished by having two types of nuclei. Of these one is single and large and is referred to as the *macronucleus*, while the second type, known as the *micronucleus* because of its small size, may be single or quite numerous — as many as eight micronuclei are present in several species. At one time the macronucleus was believed to be concerned solely with vegetative activities and the micronucleus involved in inheritance, but more recently it has been established that the larger type carries out both these functions and is indispensable. On the other hand, a specific role for the micronucleus is still undetermined; specimens from which the micronucleus has been removed both survive and multiply quite normally.[3]

### Food Habits

In the majority of the ciliates, prey is taken directly into the cell through an opening, the *cytostome*. From this structure it passes through a short tube into a *food vacuole;* after being filled the latter breaks free to circulate through the cytoplasm and receives enzymes that digest its contents. Although most members ingest such things as bacteria, yeasts, and small protozoans while swimming, a few types, including some dendroid colonial varieties, attach themselves to the substrate. Here by beating movements of the cilia, currents are set up which carry any sus-

---

[2]For a more detailed discussion of this group, refer to J. O. Corliss, *The Ciliated Protozoa*, New York: Pergamon Press, Inc., 1961.

[3]Two books are available that discuss ciliate behavior and genetics in much greater detail. These are R. Wichterman, *The Biology of Paramecium*, New York: The Blakiston Company, 1953; and V. Tartar, *The Biology of Stentor*, New York: Pergamon Press, Inc., 1961.

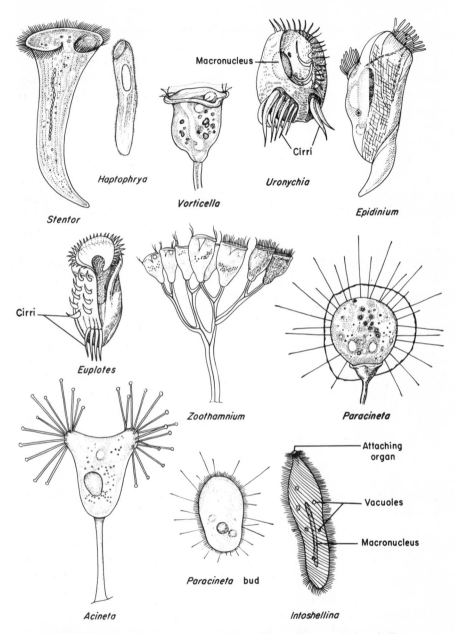

**Fig. 17.** *Diversity among the ciliates. Haptophrya* and *Intoshellina* represent the astomate types that lack a cytostome. Both *Acineta* and *Paracineta* (a bud also shown) are members of the suctorian branch. (Reproduced, with permission, from L. S. Dillon, *Principles of Animal Biology*, New York: The Macmillan Company, copyright 1965.)

pended matter toward the cytostome. In some forms, including *Stentor* and *Vorticella*, the processes of thus filtering organic matter from the medium are augmented by the funnelshape of the body (Fig. 17).

A second modification of the food habits, perhaps best illustrated by *Didinium*, occurs in a type sometimes referred to as the "hunter ciliates." These actively swimming organisms feed upon species that are nearly as large as themselves, taking in their prey whole through a cytostome placed at the tip of the proboscis (Fig. 18). To accomplish this feat, the cytostome, equipped with a number of strong ribs, is capable of being distended to the full diameter of the cell. While swimming about by means of its two encircling rows of cilia, *Didinium* changes direction

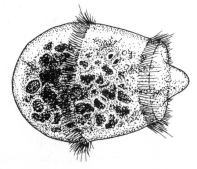

**Fig. 18.** *Didinium, one of the "hunter ciliates."*

frequently, until by accident a solid object of any sort is contacted. Then it presses its proboscis against the object and, spinning rapidly around on its long axis, seemingly attempts to bore through the substance, using the cytostone's ribs as a drill. If the contacted subject chances to be a bit of glass or wood or perhaps an organism with a thick protecting covering, the *Didinium* goes through these boring processes several times, but eventually swims away. On the other hand if it is a soft-bodied protozoan, such as a *Paramecium*, the ribs soon pierce the prey's body and then hold it fast. Once the victim has been secured, it is quickly engulfed through the fully distended cytostome directly into the cytoplasm, as no special organelle is present internally for the reception of the food. If, as sometimes happens, the ingested *Paramecium* exceeds the *Didinium* in size, the latter becomes so distended that it appears as a mere sac of cytoplasm around the other protozoan.

A third diversification in food habits is represented by a group called the *astomate* ciliates, in which the cytostome is lacking as in *Haptophrya* (Fig. 17). As these forms inhabit the intestines or other internal organs of aquatic invertebrates, the food is absorbed directly into the cell.

Still another adaptation for feeding, and probably the most outstanding of all, is that found in the *suctorians*. These organisms are looked upon as ciliates which have secondarily lost their cilia because of their sessile habits; only the young are actually ciliated and capable of swimming. After a juvenile is budded off by asexual means, it leaves the parent and swims actively for a few hours. Then, after it has encountered a favorable location, it attaches itself by secreting a short stalk, loses the cilia, and assumes the parental form. As a rule, both larval and mature individuals are provided with long, rather rigid projections called *tentacles*. Although these are armed with a knob at the tip, occasionally a second type of tentacle may be present which has sticky ends instead of terminal knobs and serves solely in the capture of prey. In most forms the food, typically other protozoans or rotifers, is caught by means of a toxic substance secreted by the knobbed tentacles. The knobs then penetrate the victim and the contents are drawn into the suctorian through the hollow stems. Just how the sucking action is produced is not clear at the present.

### D. The Sporozoans

A last major type of protozoan will be used to illustrate once more the numerous diversifications acquired by these unicellular organisms. This group, the Sporozoa, are parasites in a large variety of vertebrates and higher invertebrates. Among them are included some of the largest protozoans, one parasite of the lobster, *Porospora gigantea,* attaining a length up to 10 mm. On the other hand, some important pathogens, like *Babesia bovis,* which attacks European cattle, are as small as many bacteria, not exceeding 1 to 1.5 $\mu$ in length.[4]

Adaptation for a parasitic life is the most striking diversification found among these organisms, a specialization that is best illustrated by the causative agents of malaria belong to the genus *Plasmodium*. In man four species produce this disease, all of which have developed a highly complex life cycle in becoming adapted for their particular mode of living. The cycle may arbitrarily be considered to begin when an infected mosquito, in feeding upon a human being, introduces a number of the protozoans into the puncture. When being transmitted in this fashion the organisms are elongate, slender *sporozoites* which are capable of gliding movements. These forms migrate to the cells of the liver, into which they penetrate and assume a rounded amoeboid condition. Within the liver the pathogens undergo fission rapidly, bursting out of

---

[4]The symbol $\mu$ represents a micron, 1/1000 millimeter.

the cells periodically and entering new ones; by these processes after a week's time a large population of *merozoites* is built up. This second type of individual is then capable of penetrating red blood cells. Here in the erythrocytes the protozoans behave much as they did in the liver cells, dividing rapidly until the blood cells rupture, and entering fresh erythrocytes over and over again. During these steps a so-called "ring stage" is developed which is characteristic in form for each species (Fig. 19).

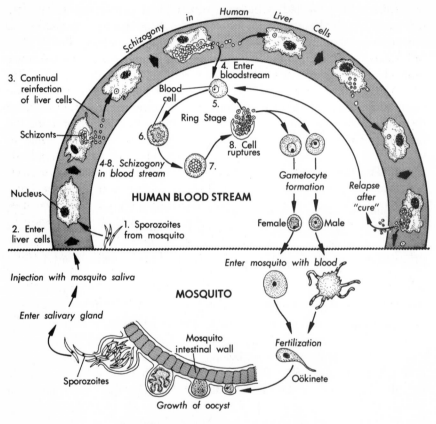

**Fig. 19.** *The life cycle of Plasmodium.*

This and comparable series of asexual reproductive processes that are carried out directly within the host's cells are usually referred to as *schizogony.* Through their employment, the organisms is capable of building up a large number of individuals from the relatively few that were originally introduced.

After a latent period of three to five days (that is, a total of ten to twelve days after infection), the first symptoms of the disease appear in the form of a series of chills and high fever. These attacks occur at intervals of forty-eight or seventy-two hours, depending on the species of *Plasmodium,* and correspond to the length of the schizogony cycle. This cycle is rhythmic, so that large numbers of infected erythrocytes are ruptured simultaneously, releasing into the blood stream in fairly large quantities the toxins formed by the merozoites.

While schizogony can continue indefinitely within the host, after five or eight days a new type of individual, the *gamont,* is produced; this stage in turn requires an additional three to six days before it is fully mature. After that period, if a gamont is taken into a mosquito's stomach during feeding, it develops into either an egg or a sperm. Still within the stomach cavity, the gametes unite to form an actively motile stage called the *ookinete.* Without aid of locomotive organelles, either flagella or pseudopods, the ookinete penetrates *between,* not into, the cells of the stomach wall; it then rounds up and secretes a covering to form a cyst. Here within this *oocyst* cell division takes place hundreds of times, resulting in the production of as many as 10,000 *sporozoites.* When mature, these rupture the wall of the oocyst and enter the body cavity of the mosquito, in which they move about until they encounter the salivary gland. After penetrating into this organ, they are ready to infect the next person the insect feeds upon. The reproductive processes within the mosquito, termed *sporogony,* differ from those of schizogony both in being initiated by sexual means and in proceeding within a sac (the oocyst) formed by the pathogen. Depending on the temperature, between ten and twenty days are required for completion of the cycle.

# CHAPTER 5

# The sponges

So highly diversified have the members of the present group, the sponges, become that their proper position relative to other forms of life has been subject of debate for more than several centuries. As will be recalled, the Greek fathers of biology avoided the controversy by placing these organisms in a kingdom separate from both plants and animals. But when the two-kingdom scheme of classification was formalized in Linnaeus' time, their relationships became an issue that remained active for at least a century, with many biologists advocating their inclusion among the plants and an equal number favoring them as animals. During the last hundred years, though the "animal" school of thought has come into ascendancy, differences of opinion concerning their relationships still persist; but contention now centers around the respective merits of considering the organisms either as an independent subkingdom, as a mere phylum among the metazoans, or as close relatives of a peculiar group of protozoans. Since no single point of view shows signs of immediately becoming universally accepted, attention will be confined here to indicating the basis for the diversity of opinion. As the description of the main features of structure, reproduction, and behavior unfolds, the student undoubtedly will agree that the wonder of the matter is, not the conflicting concepts, but the absence of even more debate.

## I. DISTINCTIVE TRAITS

For the greater part sponges are irregular in shape, without any balanced sort of body plan. or *symmetry;* however, a small number of species are vase- or cup-shaped. Since the latter types are built on a circular pattern, they may be recognized as being *radially symmetrical*. A few forms live as separate individuals, that is, they are *solitary*, but the vast majority occur as closely united groups, or *colonies*. While solitary forms are rarely more than several inches in height or breadth, the colonial varieties occasionally assume fairly immense proportions, perhaps a yard or more in diameter. Even the largest of such colonies lack the ability to react visibly to stimuli of any sort. One reason for these organisms' being considered plants in earlier days was their inability to respond animal-like even to violent blows.[1]

### Body organization

This relative inertness of the sponges arises through the absence of both nerve cells and properly arranged muscle cells. Contractile cells are present nonetheless but neither encircle nor ascend the body wall; instead they merely regulate the size of the openings into the numerous canals that penetrate the body on all sides. Beyond doubt, the canals themselves are the most striking feature of the group, their openings providing the basis for the scientific name *Porifera*, that is, pore-bearers. During the processes of diversification the canals have become organized into three distinct types of systems, called *asconoid*, *syconoid*, and *leuconoid*, the major likenesses and differences between which are shown in the illustration (Fig. 20). Often the outer surface of the body wall is covered with a layer of cells known as the *epidermis*, but the inner cavity, variously referred to as the *spongocoel* or *paragaster*, has no special lining (Fig. 21).

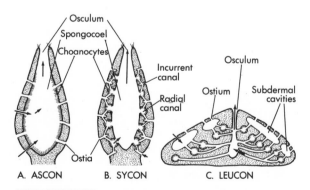

A. ASCON    B. SYCON    C. LEUCON

**Fig. 20.** *Diversity in sponge organization. In the evolution of the sponges, three major types of canal systems are developed.*

[1]An interesting account of the sponges is provided by R. Rasmont, "Sponges and Their World." *Natural History*, 71(3):62-70, March, 1962.

### Choanocytes

Within the canals proper or in enlargements of the canals, depending upon the type of system, occurs another striking feature of the sponges — the *collar cells,* or *choanocytes* (Fig. 21). It was the presence of these peculiar cells equipped with a collar and a long flagellum that first convinced biologists of the sponges' animal-like character, for the beating of the flagella induces water to flow through the canal system — in short, these cells provide active movement of a kind not usually found in plants. However, the current they set up behaves in a most unusual fashion, for the flow is *inward* through the sides and *outward* through the spongocoel's mouth-like opening, the *osculum* — quite the opposite direction from that found in fish or other aquatic creatures which are clearly animal in every sense of that word.

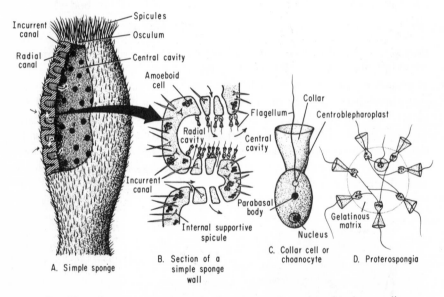

**Fig. 21.** *Sponge morphology.* As *Proterospongia* and its kin have cells constructured in identical fashion to sponge choanocytes, they are often considered distantly related to this group. (Reproduced, with permission, from L. S. Dillon, *The Science of Life.* New York: The Macmillan Company, copyright 1964.)

The "collars" or "funnels" which supply the basis for both the English and the Latin version of the cell's name appear to be food-collecting devices. Formerly it was assumed from their appearance that they might function much as funnels do. That is to say, food particles carried in the current produced by the beating flagella were thought to fall into the interior of the funnel and then possibly to be taken into the cell by pseudopodal action. Recent investigations have disclosed that this preliminary concept is at least partially correct. Instead of dropping into the interior as supposed, food particles actually adhere to the outside surface of the collar. After a particle has become attached, contraction of the collar is initiated, while the cell membrane in that region moves first upward toward the free end of the collar, and then over the upper edge, and down inside the collar toward the cell's surface, carrying the particle with it to be engulfed by pseudopodal activity.

### Other Features

After capturing food in the manner described above, the choanocyte does not seem to digest the substance itself but instead passes the particle to an amoeboid cell. Such *amoebocytes*, situated in the jelly-like matrix (*mesoglea*) which surrounds all or most of the cells of the body, engage in many of the sponge's activities. They digest food and may either pass digested materials not needed by themselves to other cells or store it in the form of fat for later consumption. Furthermore, they can become transformed into any other type of cell as required. Should a wound occur in the surface of the sponge, for example, a number of amoebocytes migrate to the area and develop into epidermal cells, sporocytes, choanocytes, or any other that may be needed to repair the injury. Finally, in addition to a function to be discussed later, that of reproduction, they may become specialized as *scleroblasts*, cells that produce the characteristic skeletal elements called *spicules*.

### Spicules

Since sponges are so comparatively simple in structure, it is fortunate for systematists who are interested in classifying them that their skeletal elements are highly diversified. Otherwise there would be little to distinguish the species or to establish relationships at the various levels represented by genera, families, and the like. As can be seen in the table (Table 3), even the classes are based primarily on these structures.

Because spicules are both extensively varied and so unusual in construction, it has been necessary to establish whole sets of terms to describe them. Subdivision based on size is first employed, with two categories, one for large and the other for small components. The larger type, called *megascleres*, form the principal skeletal framework of the

TABLE 3

A Frequently Used Scheme of Sponge Classes

| Character | Calcarea | Hexactinellida | Demospongiae |
|---|---|---|---|
| *Spicules* | | | |
| Composition | Calcareous | Siliceous | Siliceous,, spongin, or both; sometimes absent |
| Size types | Not differentiated | Megascleres and microscleres | Megascleres and microscleres often present |
| Principal types | Monaxons, triradiates | Triaxon | Tetraxon |
| *Epidermis* | Present | Absent | Present |
| *Canal systems* | Asconoid, syconoid, and leuconoid | Syconoid and leuconoid | Syconoid and leuconoid |
| *Habitat* | Shallow marine waters, particularly cooler ones | Usually deep seas, especially tropical | Shallow or deep seas and fresh waters |
| *Common name* | Calcareous sponges | Glass sponges | Siliceous sponges; horny sponges |

organisms, while the smaller spicules, the *microscleres,* are scattered throughout the body. Because much intergradation is found between the two subdivisions, the distinctions are in no way absolute ones. Nor can any such size differences be found among the skeletal elements in the Calcarea and in certain other sponges.

All spicules can be further classified according to the number of axes along which they are built. On this basis there are five chief types, most of which include varieties bearing spines at the ends. *Monaxons,* as the name implies, are built along a single axis, which may be either straight or curved; an especially frequent variety found in this category includes C-shaped ones called *sigmas* (Fig. 22). *Tetraxon* spicules, the second class, frequently have one axis elongate and three others grouped at one end of the long one, where they radiate outward in different planes. However, in a modification of the tetraxon called the triradiate, the commonest spicule of calcareous sponges, the usual long axis is nearly or entirely absent, leaving only the three lesser ones to form the same number of rays, arranged nearly on one plane.

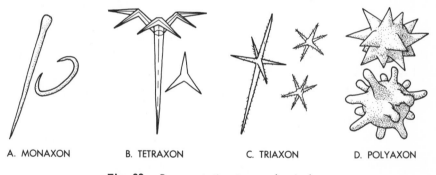

A. MONAXON     B. TETRAXON     C. TRIAXON     D. POLYAXON

**Fig. 22.** *Representative types of spicules.*

Whereas in the tetraxon type the four axes simply meet at a central point, in the third major variety, the *triaxon,* only three axes exist but cross through one another, so that six rays are formed. This type is found only among members of the class Hexactinellida. The fourth type, the *polyaxon,* consists of a large number of equal rays arranged around a central point. Usually they occur most commonly as microscleres and may be known as *asters.* The fifth type, *spheres,* are well described by their name, being rounded bodies surrounding a single point.

*Spongin.*

In place of spicules some sponges have spongin fibers, arranged in a treelike, branching fashion or in a network of sorts. Among those so constructed are the sponges sold on the market for washing windows, automobiles, or other articles. The actual sponges of commerce consist of only the skeleton; the living material is removed by the sponges' being deposited in very shallow water until the soft parts have become thoroughly decayed. In other groups a small amount of spongin may be present that serves principally in binding the spicules together. Unlike spicules, which contain large amounts of inorganic matter, spongin consists almost exclusively of a special type of protein.

## II. REPRODUCTION

In reproductive habits sponges are very varied, for they exhibit extensive powers of regeneration as well as asexual and sexual methods of propagation.

*Regeneration*

Since sponges are relatively simply organized, it is not too surprising to find that they possess great abilities in regenerating lost parts. In fact, even small pieces are capable of growing into a complete individual; the processes are so slow, however, that many months or even several years may be required for growth to be completed. But several groups of true animals, such as the flatworms and starfishes to be studied later, are similarly able to regenerate whole individuals from smaller parts. The extent of the sponges' powers is best shown by an experiment first reported by H. V. Wilson in 1907. By forcing live specimens through silk cloth, this biologist broke the organisms into isolated cells and fragments containing several cells. Under the microscope he then observed these particles as they moved about by means of the amoebocyte's pseudopodal activities. Whenever a cell or clump encountered another, fusion occurred, so that larger and larger aggregates resulted, consisting of various combinations of amoebocytes and collarless choanocytes. As the aggregates gradually became still larger, some of the amoebocytes arranged themselves in the form of an epidermis, while the choanocytes gathered into hollows and developed collars to establish typical flagellated chambers. Over a considerable period, by these processes and by ordinary growth, the fragments slowly restored themselves to a complete functional sponge.

## Asexual Reproduction

Among the asexual means of reproduction found in sponges are several which differ only slightly from regenerative processes. So similar are the two activities that the most important distinction probably lies in their origin, regeneration occurring after accidents or human experimentation, while the other is induced by climatic influences. For example, under adverse conditions, many adult poriferans may disintegrate or collapse, leaving small remnants called *reduction bodies*. Basically consisting of amoebocytic masses covered with an epidermal layer, the reduction bodies redevelop into adult sponges when favorable conditions return.

A more typical reproductive process, however, is found among all freshwater and certain marine species, in which special bodies known as *gemmules* are formed. In the freshwater sponges gemmule formation is initiated early in the fall by amoebocytes gathering into clusters here and there throughout the body. To these clustered cells, other specialized amoebocytes called nurse cells, or *trophocytes*, carry food until the former have become filled with food reserves. After fattening has proceeded sufficiently, still other amoebocytes surround the original cluster and assume a columnar shape to form a cellular wall. When completed, this living wall secretes a hard membrane over the inner and outer surfaces. In the meantime spicules are being carried to the developing gemmule and inserted between the columnar cells; distribution of the spicules is made in such a fashion that an area of the sphere is left free where a closed pore, the *micropyle*, eventually develops (Fig. 23). Soon after the gemmule has thus been completed, cold weather generally sets in and the adult sponge dies. As the old sponge disintegrates, the en-

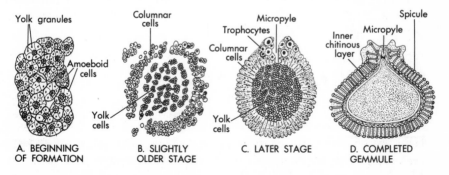

Fig. 23. *Formation of a gemmule in a sponge.*

closed gemmules are set free into the water, and, being resistant to freezing, survive the winter. In spring, after the micropyle has opened, the amoebocytes emerge and, by processes not unlike those of regeneration, slowly develop into a mature sponge.

### Sexual Reproduction

Although all types of sponges are capable of reproducing sexually, the complete details of the processes have not been clearly established. Doubt centers especially around the origin of the egg and sperm. By some biologists, the sperm, for example, has been described as being derived from an amoebocyte, but others claim it arises from a modified choanocyte. It is evident, however, that the fertilization of the egg involves a distinctive feature. At least in many species, after entering a sponge by way of the canal system, the sperm penetrates either a choanocyte or an amoebocyte, depending on the species. The latter acts as a nurse cell and actually carries the sperm to the egg, where it assists in uniting the two gametes. After fertilization is completed in this peculiar fashion, the zygote develops into a larva bearing numerous flagella; this swims about perhaps for as long as a day before attaching itself to the substrate. Once attachment is completed, the entire ciliated region of the larva infolds and thus comes to occupy the body's interior, where the ciliated cells develop into choanocytes. At the same time the remaining portion gradually forms the epidermis, mesoglea, spicules, and other parts of the adult sponge.

### III. CELLULAR TRAITS AND RELATIONSHIPS

While, as it has been seen, the sponges are amply different from the more typical animals in structure and even in the reproductive processes, still other distinctions are to be found within the cells. These unusual features of cytology are frequently employed by biologists in suggesting possible relatives of the group.[2]

### Cellular Characteristics

Although the illustration (Fig. 21) makes clear the structural features of the most characteristic sponge cell, the choanocyte, a few of the organelles present may not be familiar to the reader. The *centroblepharo-*

---

[2]A review of the problems of relationship is presented by Odette Tuzet, "The Phylogeny of Sponges According to Embryological, Histological, and Serological Data, and Their Affinities with the Protozoa and the Cnidaria," in E. D. Dougherty, *The Lower Metazoa*, Berkeley: University of California Press, 1963, pp. 129-148.

*plast,* lying at the extreme base of the flagellum, corresponds to a combination of the centriole and basal body; a second unique structure, the *parabasal body,* lies between this organelle and the nucleus. It may be recalled that a body similar in structure and name to the present one is found also in the trypanosomes. In addition to these traits, the flagellum bears two rows of flimmer.

During cell devision no trace appears of the astral rays which are so characteristic of metazoan mitotic processes; instead there is entirely distinct set of events. While the parabasal body disintegrates, the centriole separates from the blepharoplast, undergoes division, and descends to the nucleus. There each centriole secretes a new parabasal body and, at the same time, assists in the separation of the chromosomes by providing spindle threads (Fig. 24). After division is completed, the centriole ascends to, and reunites with, the blepharoplast, where it secretes a new flagellum in place of the old one.

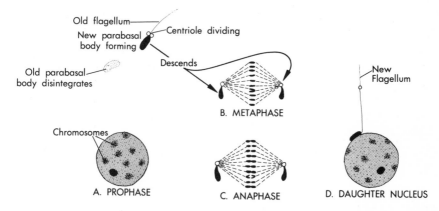

**Fig. 24.** *Cellular features of sponges.*

*Possible Relatives*

Among those unicellular forms classfied as both protozoans and algae is a group of colorless flagellates variously called the *craspedomonads* and *choanoflagellates.* These organisms are frequently regarded by biologists as possibly sharing a common ancestry with the Porifera, a suggestion based on the many unusual features shared by the cells of both groups. For instance, in these choanoflagellates is found the distinctive cytoplasmic collar of the sponge choanocyte; this structure encircles a single flagellum, which has been shown by electron microscopy to be similarly double-flimmered. Moreover, the collar has recently been observed by J. B. Lackey[3] to behave during food-catching in exactly the same manner described above for the Porifera. Resemblances are further accentuated by the cells' internal construction, for a centroblepharoplast and a parabasal body are present, arranged in a corresponding relationship with the nucleus. And finally, cell division has been shown to proceed along lines similar to those figured for the sponges.

Although most of the choanoflagellates are solitary, a few simple colonial types are also known. One of these, *Proterospongia*, is often regarded as intermediate between the two groups, though it certainly appears closer to the protozoans than to the sponges. These colonies consist of a gelatinous mass bearing scattered collared individuals embedded around the surface, while in its interior are found a number of amoeboid cells (Fig. 21).

---

[3]See J. B. Lackey, "Morphology and Biology of a Species of Protospongia," *Transactions of the American Microscopical Society*, 78:202-206, 1959.

# CHAPTER 6

# I ntroduction to metazon diversity

Although many doubts may exist about the true relationships of sponges and the unicellular organisms, there is rarely question about the metazoans proper constituting a natural close-knit group, in spite of the wide diversity that exisists. While jellyfish bear no resemblance to beetles, for instance, and lobsters look not at all like kangaroos, in between such extremes of morphology are found so many intermediate forms that all are readily discerned to be interrelated.

## I. DISTINGUISHING TRAITS

Even where species transitional in general morphology or appearance are absent, other traits are found within the bodies of all metazoans that indicate relationship. As nearly all these multicellular animals feed on living things whether of plant or animal origin, most possess a *digestive tract* to assist in the nutritional processes. Moreover, *muscle cells* that provide movement are present in very nearly every animal, and *neural cells*, with only minor exceptions, coordinate the muscle cells and the other body parts. These three traits, it must be remembered, are not only shared by the majority of metazoans but also are universally absent in every other group — including the sponges, unicellular types, and green plants as well.

Within their cells are other unusual traits which further distinguish the Metazoa. When undergoing normal division the cells display astral rays, organelles found elsewhere in identical condition solely in the brown seaweeds and in a modified state only among the primitive fungi and termite symbionts. In addition, the spermatozoa have a posterior flagellum that is devoid of flimmer, a feature shared only by dinoflagellates and the sperm of certain aquatic molds.

## II. DIVERSIFICATION IN STRUCTURE

Since so many kinds of Metazoa exist, wide diversity in internal organization might be anticipated. Nor is disappointment encountered, for variation in structure of every body organ conceivable is to be found among the representatives. In different combinations the principal variable traits are viewed as indicative of basic relationships; consequently they are used in arranging the members of this subkingdom into a number of phyla.

### Overall Plan, or Symmetry

Diversity begins with the general body plan, or *symmetry,* of the numerous types. Usually the kind of organization displayed is determined by means of a simple test, that of actually, or, more frequently, mentally, dividing the organisms into halves — mirror-image halves, to be more specific. If a knife or imaginary plane would cut the specimen into corresponding halves almost anywhere as long as it passes through a central point, the animal must be *spherically symmetrical,* for only a globe may be divided in this manner. Similarly, if mirror-image halves can be produced by any plane passing through a central line, the form in question must be constructed like a cylinder, cone, or other geometric figure based on the circle; hence, it shows the *radial* symmetry already described for sponges. Most animals, however, can be divided into two corresponding parts by only a single plane, one extending along the central axis from front to back. Since the forms are thus divided into two sides (right and left), they are said to display the *bilateral* (two-sided) variety of symmetry. Sometimes as in the snails or others with spirally built bodies, there is no possible way of dividing the organisms into mirror-image parts; consequently, in spite of a well-marked body plan, these animals are said to be *asymmetrical.*

Because the type of symmetry produces considerable differences in the general organization of the animals, distinctive sets of terminology are employed for each. For instance, bilateral animals have one end that consistently goes foremost; this is referred to as the *anterior,* while the opposite end is the *posterior.* In contrast, radially symmetrical animals are either sessile or can move in any direction, with no single region going foremost to a greater degree than any other; therefore the foregoing terms are inapplicable. For these organisms, the mouth is used as a point of reference. Accordingly the *oral* side is that surface on which the mouth is located and the *aboral*, that which lacks it. The remaining comparable terms used in describing shape and location are made sufficiently clear by the diagram (Fig. 25).

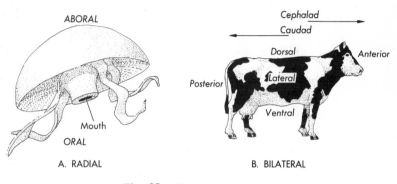

**Fig. 25.** *Types of symmetry.*

## Embryological Development

As embryology is a whole field of zoology in itself, only a summary of the principal events in development can be presented to provide sufficient background for our main topic of diversity. In all animals development is considered to commence when the sperm penetrates the egg. Once *fertilization* has thus been accomplished, the egg divides (cleaves) first into two embryonic cells, then into four, eight, and so on. Eventually these processes of *cleavage* produce an embryo known as the *blastula,* which consists of a single layer of cells. Frequently the cellular layer surrounds a cavity called the *blastocoel* (Fig. 26), but sometimes, as in snails, for example, no cavity is present.

Beyond this stage of development the details of the procedures vary extensively from group to group. Among starfish and relatives, for example, one wall of the blastula may now fold inward, forming within the blastocoel a new cavity called the *primitive gut,* which opens to the outside through the *blastopore.* In some other animals, instead of infolding, the cells divide transversely so as to fill the interior, while in still others, they migrate over top of one another. But by whatever the procedure, two layers of cells ultimately come into existence, one usually forming the primitive digestive tract and the other providing the outside

**65**

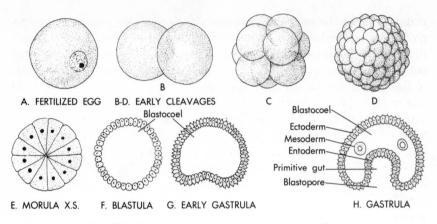

A. FERTILIZED EGG    B-D. EARLY CLEAVAGES    C    D

B

Blastocoel

Blastocoel
Ectoderm
Mesoderm
Entoderm
Primitive gut
Blastopore

E. MORULA X.S.    F. BLASTULA    G. EARLY GASTRULA    H. GASTRULA

**Fig. 26.** *Stages in the development of an embryo.*

covering. Later, as a rule, a third layer of cells develops between these two, completing the *gastrula* stage and establishing three germ layers. Named in order from the outside, these layers are the *ectoderm, mesoderm,* and *entoderm.* In a few organisms, among them the jellyfish, no mesoderm is ever established, so that only two layers are present, even in the adult. These groups are said to be *diploblastic,* while those which develop the usual three are considered *triploblastic.*

In a good many phyla, the embryo breaks free of the egg coverings and becomes an actively moving form. Such free-living *larvae* are of numerous types, as will become apparent as the various invertebrate groups are studied.

### Body Cavities

Within the interiors of the diverse animals are found cavities of many sorts, but only if other organs are enclosed within these cavities are they generally considered to be *body cavities.* Hence, although a cavity extends throughout the entire organism in such creatures as coral animals and jellyfish, it is not referred to as a body cavity because it does not enclose organs. Therefore in these organisms the cavity is given a distinctive name based on its particular functions. Since among its activities are included those of digesting and conducting food to the body cells, either the term *gastrovascular* (digestive-conductive) cavity or *coelenteron* (hollow-intestine) is most frequently applied.

True organ-containing cavities are of three major varieties. In the first and most familiar, the *coelom,* which is characteristic of earthworms, vertebrates, and others, the cavity is surrounded with mesodermal derivatives on all sides, including the outer surface of the digestive tract.[1] Frequently, a smooth mesodermal lining, the *peritoneum*, covers the entire surface, but this is not always present. The second is characteristic of the insects and their kin; in these animals the cavity contains a heart and receives blood from that organ. Hence, it plays an important role in carrying the blood and is accordingly known as the *haemocoel*. The third type, the *pseudocoel*, forms between the mesoderm and entoderm, so that the digestive tract lacks a coating provided by mesodermal derivatives; it is confined to the parasitic worms called nematodes and to related groups. Occasionally any kind of body cavity may be filled to a greater or lesser degree by loose, unspecialized tissue known as *mesenchyme*, the cells of which are frequently amoeboid.

### Homology and Analogy

When animals of various sorts are compared one with another, two major types of structural resemblances in body parts and organs are encountered, one involving fundamental, the other superficial, likenesses. On one hand, two parts which on the surface appear very different, such as a bird's wing and a human arm, may upon comparison show much in common. Inside both the wing and the arm a skeleton is found that begins with a single bone, attached to the body by a rounded knob. Lower in the two appendages a single bone is followed in turn by two long bones, a series of short flattened ones, and, finally, several rows of elongate, thin elements. When the musculature of the two appendages is examined, comparable resemblances are found; even in the origin and distribution of the nerves, veins, and arteries similarities are revealed. Body parts and organs of different species that show such general correspondence in structure are said to be *homologous* and are frequently believed to have arisen through common ancestry during past geological ages (Fig. 27).

On the other hand, if a bird's wing is compared to that of a moth, no basic structural features in common are encountered. Whereas the avian wing has a bony skeleton in the interior, surrounded by muscles which are supplied with nerves and blood vessels, the insect wing has a chitinous skeleton located on the surface and completely lacks muscle and nerves. However, because the two organs are employed for similar

---

[1]An appreciation of the coelom's importance to biology may be gained by reading three short articles on its supposed origins in E. C. Dougherty, *The Lower Metazoa: Comparative Biology and Phylogeny*, Berkeley: University of California Press, 1963, pp. 55-107.

purposes, some superficial likenesses exist. Both types, for example, provide broad expanses of surface, project to the sides, and move in a comparable manner during flight. But there all similarities cease in this and other instances of *analogous structures*. Such superficial resemblances between body parts do not reflect common ancestry but represent adaptations acquired independently for engaging in identical activities.

| Man | Dog | Bird | Bat | Insect |
|-----|-----|------|-----|--------|

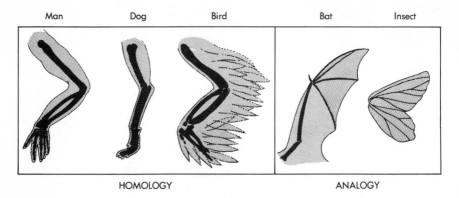

HOMOLOGY      ANALOGY

**Fig. 27.** *Comparison of homology and analogy in organs.*

### Segmentation

The bodies of many metazoans are composed of longitudinal series of more or less similar parts, called *segments,* or sometimes, *somites* or *metameres.* In some cases, while no serial arrangement is visible externally, the internal organs may nevertheless be built of repetitious series, as in the vertebral column of a fish or cat; consequently these organisms, too, are considered to be segmented.

Many variations on the general theme of segmentation exist, including its complete absence, as in snails. On the other hand, earthworms and many others are segmentally constructed both externally and internally. In contrast, insects, although distinctly segmented externally, have become so highly modified that much of the repetitiousness of structure has been lost in their internal organs. And finally, the vertebrates are distinct in lacking external segmentation but show it clearly internally in the vertebrae, ribs, nerves, and, among fishes especially, in body musculature.

## The Organism

As the various types of aimals are described in the following pages, several distinctive features of advanced forms of life in general should be noted. Because all consist of cells and cell products, in a sense they may be considered to be colonies.[2] But they are much more than merely well-organized colonies. In the first place the cells themselves are, as a rule, diversified for specialized functions, whole series of each chief type being joined together to form *tissues*, as nervous tissue for conducting impulses or as muscle tissue for producing movement. Typically tissues of several varieties are united to form *organs*, such as muscles, bones, and blood vessels, and these in turn function together in series called *systems*, whether reproductive, digestive, or circulatory.

But the whole animal, or *organism*, is not just a group of systems bound together by its integument. Far from being just the accumulation of so much digestive, neural, reproductive, muscular, and other functions, each animal, it will frequently be seen, is greater than the sum of its parts.

---

[2]A brief discussion of this concept can be found in G. O. Mackie, "Siphonophores, Bud Colonies, and Superorganisms," in E. C. Dougherty, *op. cit.* pp. 329-337. Also see A. E. Emerson, "Social Coordination and the Superorganism," *American Midland Naturalist,* 21:182-206, 1939.

# CHAPTER 7

# Some elementary metazoan types

At the very lowest levels of metazoan development, diversifications are based on lines entirely different from those encounterd among the more advanced forms. These early specializations may be viewed as experiments on Nature's part, as it were, in which an efficient manner of organization is sought. At any rate, whether the result of experiments or mere accidents, these primitive metazoans must certainly be considered aside from the main line of ascent, for reasons that will quickly become apparent.

## I. THE MESOZOA

Among the remnants of one of the earliest side branches of development is a group of organisms that are highly specialized for a parasitic mode of living. So simple are they and so distinct from the more familiar animals that they might readily pass for protozoans were their cells not provided with that identifying mark of all metazoans, the astral rays that appear during cell division. Their name is suggestive of unicellular trends, for the term Mesozoa may be translated "mid-animals," that is, between the Protozoa and the Metazoa proper.[1]

For many years, zoologists believed that these creatures might have been much more complex at one time and became degenerate as a consequence of their parasitism. Indeed, it was frequently suggested that the mesozoans were degenerate flatworms of the type called trematodes,

---

[1]The following is a brief but detailed review of this phylum: B. H. McConnaughey, "The Mesozoa," in E. C. Dougherty, *et. al. op. cit.* pp. 151-165.

to be discussed in the next chapter. But because no evidence supporting this concept has been found as the group has become better known, the trend now is toward accepting the animals for what they appear to be — extremely simple metazoans.

*Morphology*

Among the better-known mesozoans are the so-called dicyemids, a group of parasites common in the kidneys of the squids and octopi. As a whole they are wormlike animals, up to seven or eight millimeters long, whose bodies are densely covered with cilia. Each individual consists of a definite number of cells constant for each species, but usually not exceeding twenty-five. Of these, one, an elongate *axial cell*, is centrally located and surrounded by the remainder, the ciliated *somatic cells* (Fig. 28). Often the anterior somatic cells are somewhat differentiated into a *head*, the remainder of the body then being referred to as the *trunk*.

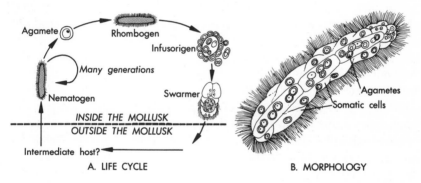

**Fig. 28.** *The life cycle and structure of a dicyemid mesozoan.*

*Reproduction*

While the somatic cells are concerned with such vegetative activities as absorbing dissolved foodstuffs from the environment, the axial cell is primarily devoted to reproduction. Although the several accounts that describe propagation disagree in some details, in general the following appear to comprise the main events: The processes begin with the axial cell nucleus undergoing mitosis. While one of these products remains unchanged to provide the axial nucleus for future generations, the second daughter nucleus in contrast undergoes numerous divisions. Large numbers of nuclei result from these mitoses, but, as cell division does not occur, the nuclei remain within a common cytoplasmic mass. Furthermore, because they are produced by simple mitosis, not meiosis, the nuclei are not looked upon as eggs but as *agametes*. After cell maturity has been attained, each agamete nevertheless behaves much as a normal egg, for further development is by growth and ordinary cell division repeated numerous times. The first division in each case is somewhat unequal, so that a larger and a smaller cell result. The larger one does not undergo further mitotic division but eventually forms the elongate axial cell of the juvenile. On the other hand, the lesser cell divides into smaller and smaller parts that gradually arrange themselves as the ciliated layer of somatic cells. After cellular differentiation has been completed, the young leave the adult's body and enter directly into the host's kidney.

### Life Cycle

As long as the host itself is sexually immature, the parasites continue to produce generation after generation of the typical form described above, called the *nematogen*. However, once the squid or octopus has fully matured, the nematogen is replaced by a second type, known as the rhombogen.[2] *Rhombogens* (Fig. 28) are produced either by modification of the nematogens existing at the period of change or directly from agametes. Basically nematogens and rhombogens are identical in structure but differ in the type of offspring they produce. Among rhombogens the agametes do not develop into new adult forms; instead they remain within the adult's body to establish a cluster of cells. These cellular balls, referred to as *infusorigens*, are themselves reproductive bodies and repeatedly give off single cells from the surface; each of these in turn undergoes multiple cleavage to form a free-swimming, ciliated *infusoriform* larva, or *swarmer*. The short, oval body of this larva consists of several central cells overlaid by a series of large outer ones, all but the two anteriormost of which bear long cilia. After completing development, the larva leaves the parental rhombogen, escapes from the host, and enters the sea. Beyond this point the cycle remains unknown; generally it is assumed that the larva infects another kind of host, where it probably matures and undergoes sexual reproduction. Then after this conjectured intermediate host has been eaten by a squid or octopus, the life cycle described above apparently begins once more.

---

[2] A semipopular account of the life cycle is found in B. H. McConnaughey and E. I. McConnaughey. "Strange Life of the Dicyemid Mesozoa," *Scientific Monthly* 79:277-284, 1954.

## II. THE COELENTERATA

How far the present phylum has become diversified from other animals is perhaps suggested by the extent of disagreement that existed in bygone years over their relationships. During the formative stages of modern biology, its members were classed along with sponges, starfishes, and an assortment of other animals in the Zoophyta. Then, after such "radiates" as starfishes had been separated into several distinct phyla, the sponges and the animals to be considered here were together designated as the Coelenterata by Leukart in 1847. It was not until 1888, however, that Hatschek finally separated the organisms into the groups usually accepted today.

Part of the difficulty over their relationships arises through the presence within this phylum of two entirely different-appearing body forms. One type, the *medusoid* represented by the familiar jellyfish, is actively swimming and more or less bell-shaped, while the other, the *polypoid*, is sessile and cylindrical. Although in some groups like the corals, sea anemones, and hydra the polypoid type alone is present and in certain

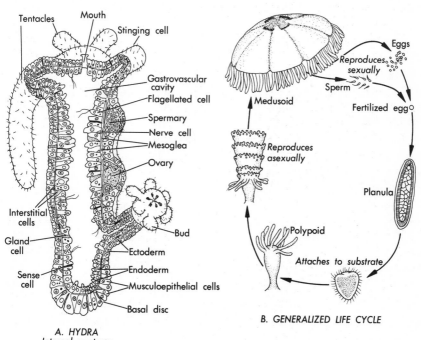

A. HYDRA
Internal anatomy

B. GENERALIZED LIFE CYCLE

**Fig. 29.** *Characteristics of the phylum Coelenterata.*

jellyfish only the medusoid, frequently both body forms are found during the course of the life cycle of a single species (Fig. 29). Frequently a distinctive flat, ciliated larva, called the *planula,* is found in the life cycle of the Coelenterata.

## A. Morphology

Although within the phylum only three major lines of development exist as reflected by that number of classes (Table 4), great diversity occurs within each class, as will be seen later. Yet, in spite of the many outward modifications, a high degree of internal structural similarity is shared by all. These fundamental characteristics are best brought out by the diagram (Fig. 28), but perhaps one point that is not self-evident requires particular notice.

### Cellular Organization

The point in question concerns the nature of the two cellular layers respectively derived from the ectoderm and entoderm in these diplo-blastic animals. Often, as by Hyman[3] for example, these creatures are considered to reflect a tissue grade of organization. If by the term "tissue" any sheetlike arrangement of the cells is implied, it is entirely applicable here. If, however, the more specific usage of zoology as defined on page 69 is meant, its appropriateness is not so evident. Notice, for instance, the number of kinds of cells found in the outside layer (Fig. 29), the so-called epidermis. Here intermixed with an epithelial type are a number of glandular, sensory, nervous, and stinging varieties. As a whole, too, the several types are not grouped together but are scattered at random throughout the layer. Within the lining of the gastro-vascular cavity, the *gastrodermis,* a similar situation is encountered. Consequently it is evident that the organization of these animals, even within the basic pattern of cell arrangement, is quite distinct from that of other metazoans. It is because of this and the other peculiarities which exist that the coelenterates are often considered to represnt a side branch, well off the main line of evolution of the Metazoa.

### Nematocysts

The stinging cells mentioned above are not entire cells, but only specialized parts, and are therefore more correctly referred to by their technical name, *nematocysts.* Normally, each nematocyst is enclosed

---

[3]Libbie H. Hyman, *The Invertebrates,* vol. I, *Protozoa through Ctenophora,* New York: McGraw-Hill Book Company, 1940, pp. 365-661.

TABLE 4

*The Classes of Coelenterata*

| Characteristic | Class | | |
| --- | --- | --- | --- |
| | Hydrozoa | Scyphozoa | Anthozoa |
| Body type | Polypoids and/or medusoids | Medusoids; polypoid reduced or absent | Polypoids only |
| Gastrovascular cavity | Not divided; not containing tentacles or nematocysts | Divided by ridges, containing tentacles or nematocysts | Divided by septa, which bear nematocysts |
| Mesoglea | Without cells | Containing cells | Containing connective tissue |
| Gonads | Ectodermal | Entodermal | Entodermal |
| Habitat | Fresh-water and marine | Marine | Marine |
| Number of species | 3,000 | 250 | 6,500 |
| Common names | Hydroids; hydromedusae; man-of-war | True jellyfish | Corals, sea anemones |

tightly within the specialized cell that secreted it. During use it is released through a trapdoor-like lid, the *operculum,* which is activated by a triggering mechanism, the *cnidocil.* After being discharged, typical nematocysts are seen to consist of a spherical or ovate *bulb,* from one end of which projects a long *thread.* Frequently at the base of the latter are several spines, but much variation in structure exists. In fact, through the detailed studies of the French invertebrate zoologist R. Weill, seventeen distinct types have been named and described. A few representatives of these are shown in the illustration (Fig. 30).

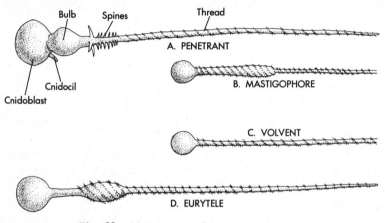

**Fig. 30.** *Major types of nematocysts.*

Not all the types are present in any single species of course; a few are common among most coelenterates, while others are confined to certain classes or orders. The familiar hydra, for example, possesses four different kinds, two of which, the *volvants* and *penetrants,* are especially abundant. The former after discharge is shaped like a corkscrew; its function seems to be that of entangling itself upon the prey, and thus assisting in the capture of food. On the other hand, the tip of the penetrant's thread, slender and too weak for the task though it may appear to be, penetrates the epidermis (even the chitinous covering of arthropods!) and, releasing its poisonous contents, paralyzes, or perhaps kills, the victim.

*Toxins of Nematocysts*

Although human beings may handle most living coelenterates without being able so much as to detect the "sting" of the nematocysts, this is not always the case. Ocean beaches are occasionally closed to bathers when jellyfish become too abundant, for a number of species produce unpleasant burns. Indeed several scyphozoans that inhabit warmer seas can cause very serious illness or even death if accidentally brushed against. The sting of the Portuguese man-of-war is similarly dangerous to human beings; contact with only a single tentacle may result in prostration, interference with breathing or, with good fortune, only severe lesions that may leave permanent scars.

These effects arise from a combination of four different sets of toxic substances that can be recognized by their solubilities in various solvents.[4] A water-soluble factor, called *hypnotoxin,* is largely anaesthetic and paralyzes the prey, whereas alcohol-soluble *thalassin* causes irritation and itching when applied to the skin of vertebrates. In larger doses, the latter induces severe gastric upsets, weakness, and death. A substance named *congestin,* which is glycerine-soluble, appears related to thalassin, for the effects of both are similar. In contrast to the first three toxins, which are proteins, the fourth is *tetramine,* that is, tetramethylammonium hydroxide. Its actions resemble those of curare in paralyzing the endings of motor nerves.

Some animals seem able to acquire an immunity against these toxins, either by heredity or by their food habits alone. The anemone, *Adamsia,* for instance, has been found to feed regularly on a number of crab species, which it stings into inactivity with its nematocyst-bearing tentacles. However, it is frequently found attached to the mollusk shell in which a certain kind of hermit crab dwells. The crab actually places the animal on its shell, in this way securing a degree of protection against predators, especially from other crabs. Moreover, the crab is known to be immune to the anemone's poison, and, if some of its body fluid is injected into other crab species, the latter become immune to the anemone's stings too.

## B. The Development of Diversity

Although the coelenterates differ in many essentials from the remaining metazoan phyla insofar as structure is concerned, they nevertheless can serve to illustrate many features of the animals in general. Not least among these is the clear-cut picture they provide of evolutionary changes

---

[4]For a discussion of poisonous marine animals in general, read B. W. Halstead, *Dangerous Marine Animals,* Cambridge, Md.: Cornell Maritime Press, 1959.

within each of several classes. While diversification is found to a comparable extent in all three classes, in two of them the developments can be made clear only by long discussions of morphological details. Consequently, here attention will be confined to the members of the class Hydrozoa which can serve as an example for all.

Of the 3,000 species belonging to this class both the majority and simplest occur among the *hydroids,* those forms that resemble *Hydra* in basic structure. *Hydra* itself is generally accepted as being included among the most primitive members — it is difficult to conceive how any animal could be much simpler in structure than it is! While that genus and others of comparable form are solitary and naked, one slightly more advanced line of development within the class establishes colonies of a peculiar sort, consisting of two distinct types of individuals. One, the *hydranth,* bears tentacles and is concerned chiefly with feeding. In contrast, the second, the *gonangium,* is usually devoid of tentacles and is specialized for reproductive purposes (Fig. 31).

The genus *Syncoryne* is primitive in that its gonangia are borne upon the hydranth, not separately. Furthermore, these individuals give rise directly to sperm or eggs, whereas more typically they reproduce only asexually by budding. The budded-off forms, moreover, do not resemble their parents, being medusoid rather than polypoid. In the present group the liberated medusoids generally are a short-lived stage; usually they do not feed and exist only long enough to shed gametes into the sea, where fertilization occurs. Since the fertilized egg then grows into a new colony of polypoids, the medusoid stage may be viewed to serve principally in disseminating the species.

Along with the above development the beginnings of another set of events occur. The colonies, as shown again by the simple genus *Syncoryne,* originally are protected by a transparent sheath only along the basal growth; with advancement this jacket, or *periderm,* becomes extended so as to provide bell-like enclosures around the hydranths and gonangia, as in *Pennaria* (Fig. 31), to mention only one of numerous types showing this structure. In other branches of the above line, instead of a chitinous covering, the colonies secrete a calcareous deposit about themselves, forming a coral-like growth. These animals, known as *hydrocorals,* grow in tropical marine waters together with true corals and make important contributions to the growth of coral reefs.

In a second major line of evolution within the Hydrozoa, the medusoid stage of the life cycle becomes accentuated, with polypoid stages reduced or even entirely absent (Fig. 31). These *hydromedusae,* or *hydroid jellyfish,* differ from the true jellyfish belonging to the class Scyphozoa in having the lower side of the bell-like body partially enclosed. The closure, formed by an ingrowing membrane or *velum* (Fig.

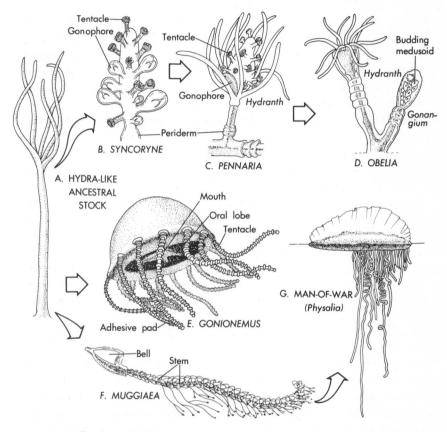

**Fig. 31.** *Diversification within the class Hydrozoa.* Three major lines of development exist. The first leads to minute attached colonies, the second ends in freeswimming jellyfish, and the third becomes modified into floating complex colonial forms.

31), assists in locomotion. As movement of jellyfish is accomplished by spreading the bell or umbrella and then forcefully closing it to expel the enclosed water, the narrow opening formed by the velum provides a stronger jetlike action and, consequently, more efficient propulsion.

Probably the most remarkable major branch of hydrozoan evolution is the third and final one, whose point of origin remains conjectural. In this line, colonialism is still more greatly developed than among the hydroids, and the colonies, rather than being attached, passively float or actively swim about the ocean. To assist in swimming, a specialized type of individual is present. The *bell* represents the most primitive specialization of this sort; from this individual, the remainder of the chainlike colony is attached, often as in *Muggiaea* (Fig. 31). With evolutionary advancement a float individual, or *pneumatophore*, is added above the bell or bells. In the simplest animals of this type, the float is small, but increased advancement it becomes very large while the bell is lost, as in *Physalia*, the Portuguese man-of-war. In these highly developed forms each apparent tentacle is really a specialized individual called a *dactylozooid*, while other types of individuals (*gastrozooids*) are modified especially for feeding. On the dactylozooids, the nematocysts are particularly well developed, and, as was pointed out earlier, are dangerous even to organisms as large as a man.[5]

## C. Distinctive Activities

### Locomotion Among Polypoids

Although hydroids are sessile, not all are permanently fixed to the substrate. *Hydra*, as an illustration, is known to move from one place to another using several different behavior patterns. If it needs to move only a short distance, it may do so by contracting and expanding the "foot," while the body remains upright. If a greater distance is involved, *Hydra* may creep in wormlike fashion along the substrate, but it has a more striking adaptation for travel — that of somersaulting. When movement of this kind is initiated, the body bends over until the tentacles touch the substrate. After the foot is released from the surface, the body inverts and loops overhead until the foot again makes contact. By repetition of these processes over and over again considerable distance may be covered.

### Movement Among Anthozoans

An interesting discovery on coelenterate behavior has recently been made by Drs. M. Pavans de Ceccatty and B. Buisson, working with a bottom-dwelling form that lives off the coast of France. This species,

---

[5]Further discussion on this branch is to be found in W. Jacobs, "Floaters of The Sea," *Natural History* 71(7):22-27, August, 1962.

*Veretillum cynomorium,* is a colonial type, reaching a length between 2 and 3 inches. Basically the colony consists of a bare "peduncle," which anchors it in the sand, and a thick prostrate "rachis," from which dozens of individual polypoids extend. The French zoologists noted that the whole colony is often involved in slow rhythmical movements, in which periods of contraction alternate with expansion, especially in response to light. While these activities are not known to move the colony from one location to another, they do demonstrate that colonial forms, even when composed of numerous individuals each capable of independent responses, can react as a single unit to changes in the environment.

Perhaps even more striking is a swimming response found during recent years in an anemone. Drs. C. S. Yentsch and D. C. Pierce, working with specimens of *Stomphia coccinea* in aquaria, observed that when certain starfish contact the coelenterate a whole set of reactions within the latter is triggered. If a starfish contacts the anemone on its oral disk, its body partially contracts and immediately reexpands. Then the entire upper portion of the animal begins a series of whirling movements, much as a human being might roll his head in a circle. Several complete rotations, each requiring about one second, may occur before the base becomes detached from the substrate. Then by undulating the body from side to side, the anemone swims tentacled-end foremost for distances up to 30 inches, after which it settles to the bottom and becomes reattached. While locomotion by this means is slow and awkward, it nonetheless provides an effective mechanism for escape from starfish.

Another recent study of movement in anemones by Drs. R. M. Ross and L. Sutton provides an insight, not into any remarkable mode of locomotion, but into the selectivity often displayed by even such primitive animals as these. The species studied, *Calliactis parasitica,* is a common inhabitant of the Atlantic Ocean off the coast of Europe, where it most frequently lives upon shells of a whelk (*Buccinum undatum*) occupied by a hermit crab (*Pagurus bernhardus*) after the seasnail has died. In earlier years it had been shown that in a different set of species, the crab (*Eupagurus prideauxi*) places the anemone (*Adamsia palliata*) upon the shell as a sort of defense, but such has not proven to be the case with the present species. The zoologists mentioned show that the present anemone actually seeks out a shell and moves onto it whether occupied by a crab or not. Whenever a shell, whether moved by ocean currents or a crab inhabitant, contacts an anemone that is attached to the ocean floor, a series of reactions is initiated. The coelenterate's body bends until several tentacles reach the whelk shell and explore its surface. If the shell is of the proper species, more tentacles extend and soon waves of tentacular movements flutter over it. Many of these organs attach, especially around the shell's margin, and such a firm hold is eventually secured that even a large crab occupant is prevented from moving its habitation farther. Once a secure hold has been established, series of contractions pass down the anemone's body, causing it to become shortened and often twisted, so that the pedal disk is gradually loosened from the substrate. After the disk has been freed, the animal bends itself nearly double as it vaults the lower end of the body onto the shell. Once located upon the shell, the pedal disk attaches firmly by means of secretions, the tentacles relinquish their hold, and the anemone resumes normal activities. Only shells of the proper species elicit the response, during which no role of any sort is played by the crab.

## III. THE CTENOPHORA

So closely allied to the coelenterates are the Ctenophora that occasionally they are placed as a subphylum of that taxon.[6] Included among the similarities are radial symmetry, jellylike mesoglea, a coelenteron or gastrovascular canal, and a two-layered pattern of organization. On the other hand, these *sea walnuts* or *comb-jellies*, as the animals are popularly called, are so distinct that today full phylum status is generally accorded them.

Probably the most striking differences are provided by the absence of nematocysts and the presence on the body surface of eight rows of *combs*. The combs are really clusters of cilia fused together to form flat platelets, which by moving back and forth provide locomotion for the organism. The beating of the combs is quite peculiar. While at rest all stand more or less upright, but in use the combs beat downward, the hindmost beating first, then the second comb, and so on to the anteriormost one in waves — quite like a row of dominoes falling over, but in reverse sequence. All then return slowly to rest before another series of beats provides forward movement again.

In spite of the radial symmetry found among these animals, the phrase "forward movement" can correctly be applied, because during swimming one end, the oral, always goes foremost. Moreover, the symmetry is modified by the presence of a pair of tentacles, each located in a pouch on the side of the body. Consequently, while the body is built on a circular pattern, it can be divided into actual mirror-image

---

[6]The question of ctenophore relationships is discussed by Taku Komai, "A note on the phylogeny of the Ctenophora," in E. C. Dougherty, *et al, op. cit.,* pp. 181-188.

halves by only a single plane. Thus modified, the animals are more strictly said to possess *biradial symmetry*.

The tentacles, often more than twice the length of the body, can be retracted into the pouches by means of muscles at their bases. Each is provided with a number of *glue cells*, or colloblasts, the secretion of which assists in capturing prey. By and large the food consists of small invertebrates, fish eggs, and plankton. Often the comb-jellies do extensive damage to oyster fisheries by consuming the larvae and thus preventing growth and replacement of the beds.

Fewer than 100 species of ctenophores are known, nearly all of which are found in the surface waters of the oceans. One of the most widely distributed forms, *Pleurobrachis pileus,* occurs in north temperate waters on both sides of the Atlantic and on the American side of the Pacific Ocean. About an inch in length and ovoid in shape (Fig. 32),

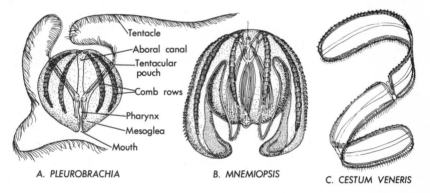

Labels in figure:
Tentacle
Aboral canal
Tentacular pouch
Comb rows
Pharynx
Mesoglea
Mouth

A. PLEUROBRACHIA     B. MNEMIOPSIS     C. CESTUM VENERIS

**Fig. 32.** *Some characteristic ctenophores.*

it is often of an attractive rose color. *Mnemiopsis leidyi,* a 5-inch long species of the west Atlantic, is transparent green; like many other comb-jellies, it is brilliantly luminescent at night. Probably the largest form is the so-called Venus' girdle (*Cestus veneris*), which, though only 2 inches wide, may reach a length of 3 feet. This Mediterranean oddity is often beautifully colored, being transparent green, violet, or blue; besides the usual locomotion provided by the comb rows, it swims by rhythmic movements of the ribbonlike body in watersnake fashion.

As a whole ctenophores are hermaphroditic. All individuals produce both eggs and sperm in gonads located in the digestive tract just below the comb plates. When mature the gametes leave the coelenteron by way of the mouth and enter the sea, where fertilization occurs. The fertilized eggs may develop either directly into the adult or indirectly by way of a peculiar larva called the cydippid. In the parasitic genus *Gastrodes*, however, a planula larva is found, providing strong additional evidence suggestive of close relationship with the Coelenterata.

# CHAPTER 8

# F alse coeloms and none

While the mesozoans and the others of unusual basic anatomy described in the foregoing chapter frequently are recognizable as metazoans only with considerable difficulty, no such problem is encountered on the animals discussed beyond this point. All hereafter are of triploblastic origin and bilaterally symmetrical, at least in the larva. Since appendages for locomotion are found only among the more advanced groups, numerous other actively motile types to be described in ensuing pages have acquired a body shape adapted for creeping movements — that, is they are of a long, slender, or wormlike form. "Worms," then, are abundant among the early phyla, but they come in many varieties.

## I. THE PLATYHELMINTHES

Probably the simplest of the wormlike phyla is the Platyhelminthes, distinguished from nearly all other metazoans by the flat, unsegmented body. This trait, in combination with absence of both a body cavity and a circulatory system, at once sets it apart from the rest, but other structural peculiarities, including flame cells used in excretion (Fig. 33), are also diagnostic.

The 13,000 species known to exist today are arranged in three classes (Table 5). One of these, the Turbellaria (flatworms), consists largely of free-living forms, found primarily in fresh and marine waters. The other two, the Cestoda (tapeworms) and Trematoda (flukes), contain only parasites, many being of economic importance in attacking either

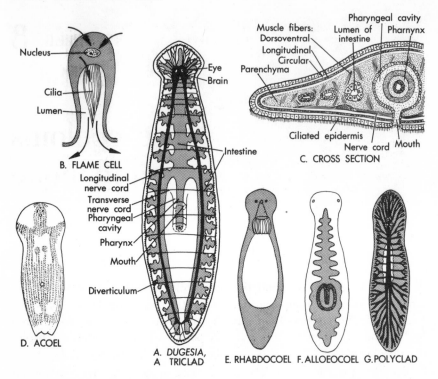

**Fig. 33.** *Morphology and representatives of Turbellaria.*

man or his domestic animals. Since the three types are so distinct in structure as well as in habit, each must be discussed separately.

### A. The Turbellaria

*Morphology*

Although the vast majority of Turbellaria are free-living in water, a few are terrestrial, and a number live upon or within other metazoans as either parasites or harmless commensals. Great diversity is exhibited even among the nonparasitic forms, particularly in the structure of the digestive tract. In one marine group, the Acoela (Fig. 33), this system consists solely of a mouth or of a mouth and pharynx, stomach and intestines being uniformly absent. In all others, while intestines are present, an anal opening is lacking; such digestive systems which do not possess an anus are said to be of the *incomplete type.*

The shape of the intestine is subject to extensive variation. It may be a simple straight sac, as in the rhabdocoels, or it may have a number

TABLE 5

## The Classes of Platyhelminthes

| Character | Turbellaria | Trematoda | Cestoda |
|---|---|---|---|
| Digestive tract | At least a mouth present | Well developed | Absent |
| Intestines | Usually present, of various form | Present, bifurcate | Absent |
| Epidermis | Ciliated, at least in part | Absent | Absent |
| Body | Undivided | Undivided | Usually divided into segments |
| Holdfast organs | Usually absent | Present, frequently with hooks | Present, often with hooks |
| Rhabdoids | Present | Absent | Present |
| Life cycle | Simple | Usually complex | Usually complex |
| Habitat | Fresh or sea water, usually free-living | External or internal parasites | Internal parasites |
| Common name | Turbellarians | Flukes | Tapeworms |

of lateral out-pocketings called *diverticula*. Sometimes the organ is divided into three major parts, as in the group called the triclads, which includes the common laboratory genera *Dugesia* and *Planaria*. Perhaps the greatest development is to be found in the polyclads, in which a large number of branches extend throughout the body (Fig. 33).

Probably the most striking feature of the turbellarians is the ventral location of the mouth at the middle of the body, instead of near the anterior end as is normally to be expected. This opening leads into a chamber called the *pharyngeal cavity*, in which lies the long, tubular *pharynx*. In such triclads as *Dugesia* and *Planaria*, the pharynx during feeding protrudes through the mouth and pumps the food into the intestine.

### Feeding Habits

Although a few acoels and rhabdocoels feed upon algae, the great majority of turbellarians eat either other small animals or bits of wounded

**87**

or dead larger forms, such as fish and clams. Despite their lack of intestines, or in many cases both pharynx and intestine, the acoels too ingest small worms and the like. While most turbellarians feed upon any kind of animal flesh, some are restricted to particular items. For example, a polyclad named *Stylochus* that occurs along the Atlantic coast of southeastern United States lives solely on oysters, and some fresh-water planarians consume only live water fleas.

Live prey appear to be detected by turbellarians mainly by direct contact or the disturbance in the water resulting from the prey's movements. Once the food has been located and approached, the turbellarian secures a hold by means of adhesive organs on its head and, after encircling the animal with its body, employs secretions from the various epidermal glands in entangling and subduing the prey to a state of helplessness.

In running water, flatworms detect juices from dead or wounded animals at considerable distances. If a fish head or a piece of uncooked meat is placed in a shallow stream, downsteam the planarians can be observed emerging from beneath leaves or stones in large numbers and crawling toward the bait. Upon reaching the meat and testing it thoroughly with their chemical receptor organs, the planarians creep partially upon it and protrude the pharynx through the mouth. Only if the bait is large do the planarians crawl completely upon it; otherwise they keep at least a portion of their body attached to the substrate by means of secretions.

Ingestion varies with the type of planarian. In polyclads and certain others, the prey is swallowed whole by rhythmic muscular contractions in the pharynx, the latter becoming greatly distended during the processes. But more typically the pharyngeal contractions merely provide suction so that the prey is taken in bit by bit.

### Digestion

The processes of digestion in these worms may be indicative of their general level of development. Digestive activities probably are confined entirely to the intestine, where they proceed in a most unusual fashion. Instead of secreting a digestive juice, the enzymes of which act upon ingested food, as in most animals, the intestinal cells engulf the material themselves. If a series of planarians are fed some beef, for example, and sections for microscopic study are made at intervals over several days, these cells are found to become active as soon as food contacts them. By intake of some of the water which enters the tract along with the food, they increase in size until they bulge into the intestine's cavity (Fig. 34). Here they may fuse into a plasmodium, or, as often as not, remain solitary. In either case, they send out pseudopods and engulf the food in amoeboid fashion, forming food vacuoles similar to those of protozoans. About eight hours are required to empty the food from the intestine, and another period of similar duration is necessary to condense the vacuolar contents into homogenous masses. These masses are then gradually digested within each cell, the processes requiring perhaps five days for

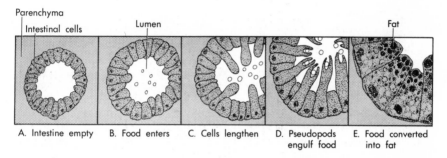

Parenchyma | Intestinal cells | Lumen | Fat

A. Intestine empty    B. Food enters    C. Cells lengthen    D. Pseudopods engulf food    E. Food converted into fat

**Fig. 34.** *Activities of the intestinal cells during digestion.*

completion. As the proteins disappear, a series of fat droplets accumulates in the outer portion of the cells and is stored for future use. Apparently the worms are incapable of digesting carbohydrates and therefore derive their energy from the fats, which in turn are formed from proteins. Nothing appears to be known of the processes by which digested and stored foods are conveyed to the other parts of the body.

## B. The Trematoda

### Morphology

In contrast to the turbellarians, the *flukes* that comprise the class *Trematoda* vary not at all in the structure of the digestive tract. Perhaps this constancy stems from the worm's parasitic habits, as all species live either upon or within the bodies of other metazoans, particularly the vertebrates. Probably associated with their mode of life, too, are their most striking external features, the disks, spines, and suckers by means of which they cling to the host. Even the name of the class is based on these holdfast structures, for its stem, the Greek word *trema*, means "hole" and refers to the pit of the suction disk.

Holdfast mechanisms are of three major types, a fact that is employed by systematists in classifying these worms into orders. These differences, summarized in Table 6 and illustrated in Figure 35, are associated with other distinctive traits, such as the method of parasitizing the host and the often highly specialized life cycle.

TABLE 6

*The Orders of the Trematoda*

| Character | Monogenea | Aspidobothria | Digenea |
|---|---|---|---|
| Oral sucker | Absent | Absent | Well developed |
| Ventral sucker | Well developed, located posteriorly | Well developed, located medially | Usually present, varied in location |
| Hooks | Present | Absent | Absent |
| Excretory pores | Paired, anterior, dorsal | Single or double, posterior | Single, posterior |
| Mode of life | Ectoparasites | Endoparasites | Endoparasites |
| Alternation of hosts | None | None | Marked |

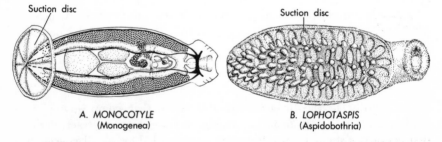

A. *MONOCOTYLE*
(Monogenea)

B. *LOPHOTASPIS*
(Aspidobothria)

**Fig. 35.** *Representatives of two orders of trematodes. For an example of Digenea, see Fig. 37.*

## The Life Cycle of Monogenea

In the Monogenea, development is quite simple, especially among the common ectoparasitic species. The eggs after deposition become attached by means of threads to the fish's gills on which most of the worms feed; after hatching, the juveniles grow more or less directly into the adult form. This basic pattern, however, often shows specializations which have been acquired in adapting to the parasitic existence.

For one example the endoparasitic genus *Polystoma*, which lives in the urinary bladder of frogs, may be cited. In spring, this fluke releases its eggs into the frog's bladder, which they leave with the excreta into the water. After about four weeks time, the larvae hatch and attach to the gills of tadpoles that are nearly ready to undergo metamorphosis. At first the larva is quite distinct from the adult *Polystoma* (Fig. 36). On the dorsal surface are four eyes, while the entire epidermis is covered with transverse bands of cilia. The attachment organ is especially distinct in bearing numerous hooks, but no trace exists of the six suckers

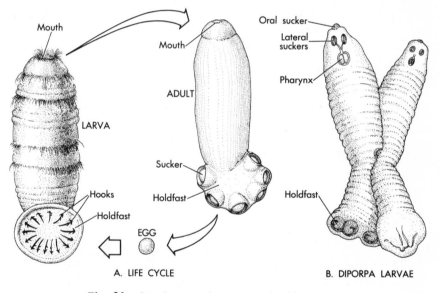

**Fig. 36.** *Developmental stages in the Monogenea.*

that characterize the mature fluke. After the tadpole has metamorphosed into a frog, the larva passes down the digestive tract and enters the bladder through the cloaca. It then completes development by losing the eyes and the ciliated epidermis and by gaining one pair of suction disks at a time upon the holdfast until the normal three pairs have been acquired. In the meantime the hooks disappear or become incorporated into the suckers.

Some of the gill-dwelling forms, too, show peculiarities of development. In *Gyrodactylus*, for instance, after the original embryo has developed to a certain point within the egg, a second embryo forms inside it. When the second has similarly reached a suitable stage, a third embryo may grow within the second, and, frequently, a fourth may appear within the third. Hence, a single egg may give rise to as many as four embryos. After completing its development, the first embryo hatches, still with its fellows enclosed, and attaches directly to the host. In turn the second, enclosing the later embryos, emerges when ready from the first and commences feeding, the third and fourth leaving their immediate predecessor in similar fashion. This adaptation, besides being striking, throws light on some developments found later among the Digenea.

But the most curious diversification is that shown by members of the genus *Diplozoon*. After emerging from the egg and losing such early larval features as eyes and cilia, the immature animal attaches to fish gills and begins to develop into a second larval stage known as the *diporpa*. A suction disk forms centrally on the ventral surface while at a corresponding position dorsally a papilla appears. Two diporpa larvae then unite, one using its midventral sucker to grasp the mid-dorsal papilla of the other. As the bodies of the pair do not lie completely superimposed, they cross over one another in the form of an X. Lying in this position the bodies of the two flukes permanently fuse; even the reproductive systems become joined together so that the sperm formed in one individual flows directly into the other, insemination being reciprocal in these bisexual organisms.

### The Life Cycle of the Digenea

Probably nowhere else in the animal world are adaptations for an endoparasitic mode of living so complex as in the life cycle of the Digenea. As a rule during development four distinct kinds of larvae occur in sequence and these usually parasitize three, or sometimes even four, different species of animals. The final host is most frequently a vertebrate, including fresh-water, marine, and terrestrial species, while the first host typically is a mollusk such as a clam or snail (Fig. 37).

Some of the features of larval development recall certain of those fond in the Monogenea, including the presence of eyes and ciliated epidermis on the first larva. As the eggs are usually deposited in water, this larva, the *miracidium*, after hatching swims actively until it encounters a suitable host. Often a snail of a definite genus or even species

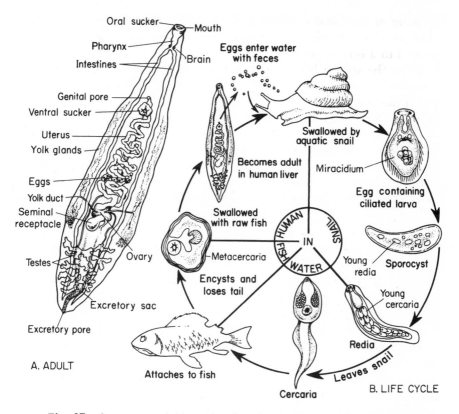

**Fig. 37.** *Structure and life cycle of a digenetic trematode. The Chinese liver fluke provides the example here.* (Reproduced, with permission, from L. S. Dillon, *Principles of Animal Biology*, New York: The Macmillan Company, copyright 1965.)

is parasitized, but sometimes bivalves serve as this first intermediate host. Being quite minute (0.2 mm in length), the miracidium is incapable of surviving longer than twenty-four hours as a free-living form. If fortunate in encountering a host soon enough, the larva enters its body by dissolving a hole through the flesh using enzymatic secretions from special organs called *penetrating glands*. Either during passage into the host's body or shortly afterward, the miracidium sheds its entire epidermis, including the cilia and eyes, to develop into the second larval type, the sporocyst.

*Sporocysts* vary extensively in shape, ranging from wormlike to rounded or highly branched and up to an inch in length. Unlike the miracidium from which it is derived, the sporocyst's body is hollow but

93

still shows no trace of a digestive tract. At this stage the parasite moves freely through the host tissues and often does extensive damage. In the meantime special bodies, called *propagative cells* or *germ balls,* show a resemblance to the monogenetic *Gyrodactylus* discussed earlier. These cells, located posteriorly in the cavity, produce other embryos, either daughter sporocysts or larvae of the next type, each of which in turn contains its own set of propagative cells within it.

The next larval stage, the wormlike *redia,* differs most strikingly in appearance from the preceding in having a collar near the anterior end and two projections on the ventral surface. Probably the most notable distinction, however, is the presence of a digestive tract. This system is quite simple and consists only of a mouth, a muscular pharynx, and a saclike intestine. The birthpore is another new feature; this opening leads from the interior and provides an exit for the products of the propagative cells.

The propagative cells give rise either to a second generation of redia or, more frequently, a very distinctive type of larva named the *cercaria.* After exiting through the birthpore, the cercariae penetrate the host's body wall and enter the surrounding water. With their broad rounded bodies and thick tails, these worms resemble tadpoles on a minute scale, the body rarely exceding 0.02 inch in length. Internally the anatomy is far more complex than that of any preceding stage. The digestive tract, like that of the adult, consists of a mouth surrounded by an oral sucker, a pharynx, an esophagus, and a bifurcated intestine. The excretory system, too, is similar to the adult's, but the bladder opens into a tubule which extends nearly to the tip of the tail. Just before the apex, however, it divides into two, to end in a pore on each side. Depending on the family, the tail is often highly specialized; in certain forms it may be forked much like a fish's and in others it is coated with long hairs.

A cercaria swims about for a period varying from a few minutes to as long as three days before encysting either upon or within a second intermediate host. This host may be nearly any type of metazoan, including jellyfish, annelid worms, flatworms, crabs, lobsters, insects, and fish, but it is frequently specific for any stated type of fluke. Entrance into this host is affected by means of the penetration glands and a sharp rostrum; generally during these processes of entering the tail is shed. Once inside, the cercaria secretes a thick wall around its body and remains inactive as this cystlike *metacercaria* until the host chances to be eaten. If the predator proves to be the definitive host of the trematode, the cyst ruptures, and the young gradually matures after reaching the host organs for which it is adapted.

Reexamination of the foregoing cycle discloses that great odds exist against a given egg producing a larva that will reach maturity. First, since the adults live internally and often in terrestrial organisms, the eggs depend upon favorable wind or rain to reach the water needed for successful hatching. Second, that water must contain healthy representatives of the first intermediate host, usually members of a particular genus or even species. Third, the minute miracidium needs to encounter one of these within the short span of its free life. Fourth, suitable examples of the second intermediate host need to be available for the cercaria when it emerges, and, finally that host must be eaten by the definitive host, often of a specific nature. And it should be remembered that these hazards are additional to all the others to which animals in general are subject, such as predation and disease. Consequently, the chief advantages of the cycle to the species lies in the abundance of end products which ultimately derive from any single successful miracidium. Although that first larva typically gives rise to only one sporocyst, the latter engenders numerous rediae, each of which in turn produces a profusion of cercariae by means of the propagative bodies. According to calculations made by Libbie Hyman, a single fertilized egg on the average may in indirect fashion result in as many as 10 to 50 thousand cercariae.

## C. The Cestoda

Like the flukes, the *tapeworms* that comprise the present class are highly specialized for an endoparasitic existence, and similarly lack epidermis and accompanying cilia. Eyes, too, are absent, but in the cestodes they are never present, not even in the larvae as among the trematodes. Moreover, parasitism is obligatory in tapeworms because a digestive tract is absent during the entire life history.

Still further likenesses to the Trematoda exist, but these are usually looked upon as parallel developments acquired independently in the two classes as adaptations for the same kind of life. Included among these is a complex life cycle, involving as many as three different host species, and organs for attachment to the host body. That these are separate acquisitions is suggested by the evolutionary diversifications found within the present class, as will be seen below.

### Morphology

As a whole the tapeworms are more extensively diversified in body morphology than the Trematoda and display a greater range in size, some being only a few millimeters long whereas others reach 18 meters.

The flat body is either simple or divided into numerous segments called *proglottids* (Fig. 40). When proglottids are present, an unsegmented *scolex* at the anterior end of the worm functions in attaching the organism to the host and forming new proglottids.

Both a digestive tract and body cavity being absent, the scolex and proglottids internally consist of muscle and mesenchyme surrounding the nervous and excretory organs. These systems, shown diagrammatically in Figure 40, need no further discussion here, except to indicate that the reproductive organs are confined to the proglottids. It is thus apparent that the scolex produces proglottids asexually by budding, while the latter carry out sexual propagation.

### Holdfasts

Among the main specializations of the scolex are the external structures used for securing a hold onto the lining of the host's organs. Development of such holdfast structures is represented by an evolutionary

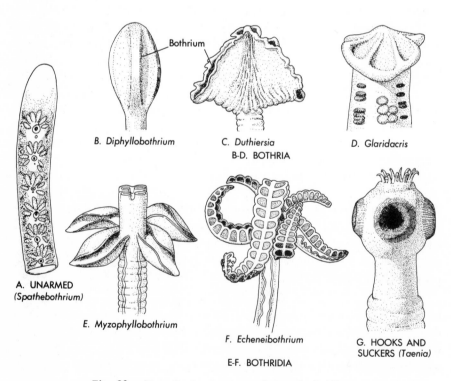

**Fig. 38.** *Diversity in structure of cestode holdfasts.*

series that begins with their complete absence. In *Spathebothrium*, for one illustration, the head is differentiated from the remainder of the worm by lacking reproductive organs, but both it and the entire body are devoid of external features for anchorage (Fig. 38). Probably the first holdfasts are the simple grooves on the sides of the scolex, like those found in *Diphyllobothrium*, one species of which is parasitic in man (Fig. 38). *Bothria*, as such grooves are called, are in general provided with few muscles. Of the many varieties that are known, the most extremely diversified is probably the frilly folded organ found in *Duthiersia*; but another interesting series develops multiples of the folds side by side, as in *Glaridacris* (Fig. 38).

Perhaps derived from the last variety is the second major type of holdfast, known as the *bothridium*. These leaflike extensions of the scolex wall are often arranged in groups of four around the anterior end. In its most elementary form each extension bears a simple groove as in *Myzophyllobothrium*, but with advancement the groove becomes subdivided to form two or so chambers. Further subdivision culminates in the very elaborate organ found in *Echeneibothrium* (Fig. 38).

True *suckers*, circular depressions in the scolex wall, are similarly arranged in groups of four. Equipped with several sets of muscles, suckers can create a strong vacuum to attach to the smoothest lining of a host organ. *Taenia solium*, the beef tapeworm of man, for example, is quite capable of maintaining its position on the slippery mucosa of the human intestine and is dislodged only with considerable difficulty. The pork tapeworm, however, is perhaps assisted by the ringlet of *hooks*, the fourth and final type of holdfast found among tapeworms (Fig. 40).

### Typical Life Cycle

So frequently, often as a matter of necessity, is the life cycle of *Taenia solium* given as the sole example in introductory biology courses that a beginning student is not aware of the specialized nature of that species. Actually the basic pattern is far better shown by another parasite of man, the broad tapeworm (*Diphyllobothrium latum*), which will provide the illustration here (Fig. 39).

In this species and in the majority of tapeworms, the eggs develop to maturity within the proglottids, which in the meantime have become detached from the unripe segments and have passed to the outside along with the host's feces. After the proglottid wall has disintegrated, some eggs by action of wind or rain eventually reach a pond. Here hatching occurs, and the ciliated *coracidium* swims about for a time. This stage

**97**

must be eaten by the first intermediate host (usually a crustacean) to undergo development into the second larva, the *oncosphere*. After entering the crustacean's body cavity, this new larva develops into the *procercoid,* which remains inactive unless its host is swallowed by a fish or other vertebrate. In the second host the procercoid becomes modified into the fourth larval type, the *plerocercoid;* the latter then becomes quiescent until a third host, such as a larger fish, bird, or mammal, consumes the second host. Here the plerocercoid attaches to the intestinal lining, where it increases in length to become a fullgrown tapeworm. In this location it absorbs digested foodstuffs through its body wall and forms many proglottids each day.

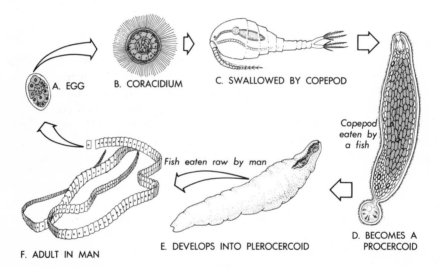

A. EGG    B. CORACIDIUM    C. SWALLOWED BY COPEPOD

Copepod eaten by a fish

Fish eaten raw by man

F. ADULT IN MAN    E. DEVELOPS INTO PLEROCERCOID    D. BECOMES A PROCERCOID

**Fig. 39.** *Life cycle of Diphyllobothrium lata.* This broad tapeworm of man has a life cycle like that of most species of cestodes.

### Life Cycle of Taenia

Among more specialized tapeworms such as *Taenia,* the foregoing cycle has been adapted to a life in terrestrial hosts, largely through elimination of certain stages and modification of others. For instance, the free-swimming coracidium phase is passed in the egg or as a membrane-covered embryo. Hence, the first larva is the *oncosphere,* which breaks free of the coverings after being swallowed by an intermediate host. Subsequent penetration through the host's intestine and entrance into muscles or other organs are similar to the basic pattern, but the procercoid and plerocercoid stages are together condensed then into a *cysticercus*. This larva first forms an oval, hollow cyst, one end of which folds inwardly. Inside this invagination develop the suckers and ring of hooks which characterize the scolex later (Fig. 40). If the intermediate host is fed upon by the final one, the invagination turns inside out, the bladder-like portion is shed, and the scolex commences production of proglottids after attachment to the intestinal wall has been made.

## II. THE NEMERTINEA

The *ribbonworms* that constitute the 600 known species of the phylum Nemertinea are not too unlike certain free-living Platyhelminthes in appearance, except that the body tends to be less flattened. Similarly a distinct head, all trace of segmentation, and a body cavity are absent. But there all resemblances cease.

Most nemertineans are free living on the ocean bottom, but a number occur in fresh water, and a very few are terrestrial. The name ribbonworm refers as much to their attractive colors as to their slender form. The dorsal surface of many species is green, patterned with contrasting stripes or bands, while others are variously pigmented with red, brown, or orange. The range in body length is exceptional, the maximum size for a species varying from a few millimeters to as much as 30 meters in *Lineus Longissimus* from the North Sea.

### Morphology

Outstanding among the traits that distinguish the members of this phylum from those of the preceding is the presence of a complete digestive tract. Aside from the addition of an anal pore, the tract is quite similar to that of the Platyhelminthes, the intestine often bearing sets of diverticula along the entire length. A circulatory system provides a second major distinction; this is of the closed type — that is, the blood remains within vessels throughout the body. Some of the longitudinal vessels are contractile and serve as hearts to pump the blood throughout the system. Usually the blood is colorless but may be red, yellow, green, or orange, depending on the species. The blood cells are of the white type, except in red-blooded species, where special corpuscles carry hemoglobin.

### The Proboscis Apparatus

While the other structural features are sufficiently clear in the illustration (Fig. 41), one peculiarity, the *proboscis apparatus*, requires at-

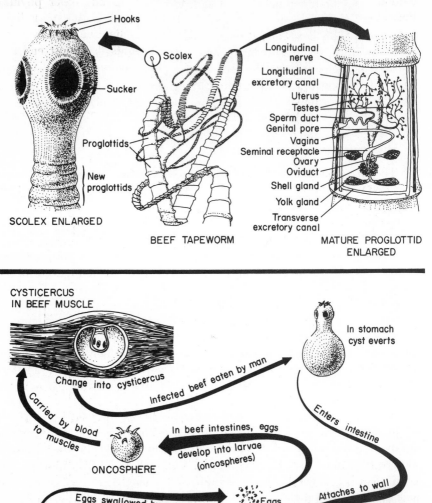

## A. STRUCTURE

Hooks

Scolex

Sucker

Proglottids

New proglottids

SCOLEX ENLARGED

BEEF TAPEWORM

Longitudinal nerve
Longitudinal excretory canal
Uterus
Testes
Sperm duct
Genital pore
Vagina
Seminal receptacle
Ovary
Oviduct
Shell gland
Yolk gland
Transverse excretory canal

MATURE PROGLOTTID ENLARGED

CYSTICERCUS IN BEEF MUSCLE

In stomach cyst everts

Change into cysticercus

Infected beef eaten by man

Carried by blood to muscles

Enters intestine

In beef intestines, eggs develop into larvae (oncospheres)

ONCOSPHERE

Eggs swallowed by cattle

Eggs

Attaches to wall

Ripe proglottids leave with feces

MATURE PROGLOTTID

Grows in length and matures

B. LIFE CYCLE

**Fig. 40.** *The life cycle of Taenia solium.* The beef tapeworm of man is representative of the highly advanced cestodes. (Reproduced, with permission, from L. S. Dillon, *Principles of Animal Biology*, New York: The Macmillan Company, copyright 1965.)

tention because nothing identical to it is found in any other phylum. Basically it consists of the *rhynchocoel,* a fluid-filled cavity that is lined with a *proboscis sheath.* Within the rhynchocoel lies the *proboscis;* essentially this organ is a muscular tube, closed at its innermost end and often twice the length of the body. Except for a slender muscle fastened

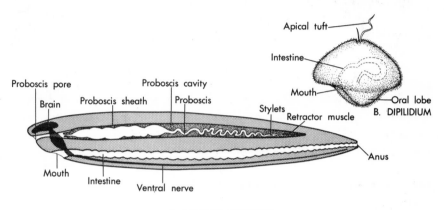

A. INTERNAL ANATOMY

**Fig. 41.** *Characteristic features of the Nemertinea.*

to the closed end, it is attached only at the anterior pore through which the cavity opens to the outside. In many species it is provided posteriorly with set of sharp hooks or stylets.

The proboscis, employed principally in capturing food, also serves as an effective defense mechanism. When used for either purpose, it is shot out through the pore explosively by means of pressures exerted upon the rhynchocoel's fluid by contractions of the proboscis sheath. The action can best be understood by comparison to a rubber glove. If such a glove is inflated lightly and one finger pushed back into the hand portion, the finger turned inward corresponds to the proboscis at rest. Now if strong pressure is placed upon the glove's hand, the finger is ejected quite forcibly, as it resumes its usual position. The proboscis differs in that normally it lies within the cavity; hence when it is expelled by muscle contraction, it actually becomes turned inside out. Any stylets present in the interior thus are pointed outward at the extreme tip after eversion, and can assist in capturing and holding prey. After the animal has been eaten, the proboscis is withdrawn into the rhynchocoel by means of the slender retractor muscle.

*Reproduction*

Although a small number of hermaphroditic species are known, the greatest majority have the sexes separate. Usually the eggs, enclosed in a gelatinous sheath, are deposited in the water for fertilization. In many ribbonworms the fertilized ovum develops directly into a juvenile that resembles the adult, but in a number of others it gives rise to a distinctive larva called the *pilidium*. The pilidium, whose entire surface is covered with short cilia, bears an *apical tuft* of long cilia at its upper pole (Fig. 41); this tuft and the thickened epidermis to which it is attached forms the *apical organ*, the total larval nervous system. While basically bell-shaped, the larva possess an oral lobe on each side of the mouth which gives it an appearance reminiscent of a soccer or football helmet. Internally the anatomy is extremely simple, the digestive tract being the most prominent feature. This system consists of three parts only: the mouth already mentioned, a foregut, and an intestine. No anal opening is present. After swimming actively for a few days, the pilidium undergoes metamorphosis and becomes a juvenile ribbonworm.

## III. THE NEMATHELMINTHES

In some schemes of classification the Nemathelminthes together with those that follow in this chapter are combined into a single phylum under the name Aschelminthes. Other zoologists feel that the relationships are better expressed if each type is treated as a phylum in its own right. All, however, agree that together they form a natural unit, for the various components share an unusual trait found nowhere else, an unlined body cavity, the *pseudocoel*.

The present group, whether considered a class or phylum, includes more than 10,000 known species of slender worms called *nematodes*. While numerous species are free living, more attention has been given the parasitic forms, which are common not only in all vertebrate groups but in cultivated plants as well. Most free-living varieties are very small or even miscroscopic, as a rule being under 1 mm in length; a few marine nematodes are exceptional in attaining a length of 50 mm. On the other hand, the parasitic species, while mostly small or moderate in size, may in some cases reach a length of a meter or more. All have whitish, dull yellowish, or transparent bodies.

*Morphology*

Except for a few species in which the females are short and ovate in form, nematodes are elongate, slender worms with unsegmented bodies, often pointed at both ends. As a whole the structure is relatively simple (Fig. 42) and includes a straight *digestive tract* consisting only of a mouth, pharynx, intestine, and anus. The *pharynx* is a most characteristic feature, for it is triangular in cross section instead of round as in most animals. The *excretory system* is also unique in consisting solely of two tubules; flame cells and nephridia, the characteristic excretory organs of other phyla, are entirely wanting.

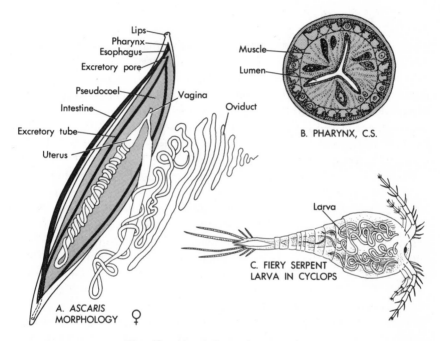

**Fig. 42.** *Morphology of nematodes.*

Another distinction similarly involves the absence of a structure of widespread occurrence among animals, in this case cilia. No cilia of any type occur in embryonic, juvenile, or adult nematodes; even the sperm cells are devoid of cilia and travel by amoeboid movement. The *nervous system* is composed of four main longitudinal cords, each with a few ganglia. No brain is present, but the longitudinal cords are interconnected by a commissure, the *circumenteric ring,* which encircles the pharynx.

103

After embryological development has been completed, cell division ceases except in the reproductive system, the number of cells present in other regions and systems being constant for each species. All growth of the young thus depends on increase in the size of the cells. As the body is covered with tough cuticle, growth, like that of insects, involves molting of the old covering; usually four molts occur during the course of the life history. Unlike most worms, the body wall consists of an epidermis only, with scattered fibers of muscle; hence, the cuticle appears to assist in support as well as in providing protection.

## Plant Parasites

Basically the nematodes parasites of seed plants are soil inhabitants which have become diversified to a greater or lesser extent for existence in or upon plants. The most elementary stage in development of phyto-parasitism is shown by those soil species whose juveniles merely attach externally to roots and feed on the juices. A greater advance toward development of the habit is found in species whose juveniles may either live free in the soil or penetrate into plant tissue and there develop into adults. The young from such adults escape into the soil and may or may not parasitize a plant, depending on circumstances, not heredity.

On the other hand, at the highest stage of specialization, parasitism is obligatory. This level is best exemplified by *Tylenchus tritici*, which infests wheat. The young of this species penetrate a growing wheat plant and ultimately reach the flowering head, where they grow to maturity and begin to reproduce. As each female produces several hundred juveniles, a thickening called a gall gradually forms where wheat grains normally would. With the approach of winter the adults die while the larvae remain in the gall. Since wheat plants usually become prostrate by spring, the larvae readily leave the gall then and penetrate the soil to infest young wheat plants as new growth is initiated. Should the gall, however, fail to reach the ground, the juveniles show a remarkable resistance to desiccation; wheat galls as old as twenty years have released living nematodes when opened.

## Animal Parasites

Among the most important nematode parasites of man are the hookworms of the genera *Ancylostoma* and *Necator*, the former being largely Old World and the latter New World. The life cycles of the two are nearly identical. The adults live attached to the intestinal walls of the host, sometimes in such numbers as to appear like the pile of a rug.

Here they feed on the tissues of the intestine, frequently rupturing the walls of capillaries and causing such loss of blood that the host becomes anemic. The numerous eggs each female produces pass out of the body along with feces. Should the latter be deposited on soil, the eggs hatch into minute "larvae" (actually juveniles), which feed on the organic matter. After two molts, they reach the infective stage when they remain on the surface of the ground, awaiting contact with the bare skin of a passing human being. After penetrating the skin, the young enter the lymphatic system and are carried through the vessels to the heart. Then migrating through the blood stream they enter the lungs, from which they pass up the trachea and into the digestive tract by way of the epiglottis. In the intestines they grow rapidly to the adult stage after two additional molts. Adults are known to remain active for as long as twenty years.

Probably the most specialized of the nematode parasites are those which require an intermediate host, usually an insect or other arthropod. Among these the most interesting is possibly the "fiery serpent" which receives mention in biblical accounts. The infective larvae live in water fleas, a kind of minute crustacean that abounds in fresh water (Fig. 42). If a water flea is accidentally swallowed by a human being in drinking water, the larvae leave their first host and penetrate through the intestinal tract of the second. After reaching the subcutaneous tissue they mature and increase in length as they migrate from one body part to another. Still beneath the skin, fertilization may occur, after which the males perish while the females form a blister or abscess, most frequently on the host's legs or back. Within this blister the female lies with the vagina adjacent to a central opening; through this she pours out thousands of living young when the lesion becomes wet, as during bathing. These juveniles swim about until, encountering a water flea, they penetrate into the arthropod, where they become semidormant.

### IV. THE NEMATOMORPHA

Sometimes the "horsehair snakes" that constitute the Nematomorpha are treated as the class Gordiacea within the Nemathelminthes, but more often they are ranked as a separate phylum. Whatever the scheme of classification, these worms bear obvious relationships with the nematodes, for many structural similarities are shared by the two taxa. The elongate slender body, in shape not unlike that of the preceding phylum, ranges from 100 to 700 mm in length and from 0.3 to 2.5 mm in diameter. Frequently the cuticle is tan or brownish, but the color varies extensively even within species. Adults are free living in fresh-water habitats, but the larvae are parasitic in insects.

Among the major distinctions between the horsehair snakes and nematodes are the complete absence of an excretory system and the degeneracy of the digestive tract. Usually the tract is represented largely by a cloaca, to which is also attached the reproductive system, opening near the posterior end by way of an anus. Frequently even a mouth may be wanting and no trace of a triangular pharynx is ever found; a reduced pharynx and a mouth however, do exist in the genus *Nectonema* but do not attach to the cloaca.

### Life Cycle

In the larva the digestive tract is reduced to even a greater degree, for at most a short posterior intestine and anus are present. The absence of a mouth in the larva is more striking because the eversible proboscis on the anterior end appears designed for feeding. However, no opening exists through which ingestion could possibly occur; so the organ functions only in penetrating host tissues. The larvae hatch from eggs deposited in water and, according to Dorier, secrete mucus in which they encyst. Here they may lie for some time until swallowed by the proper host, usually a cricket, grasshopper, beetle, or roach. Perhaps cysts are taken in while the insect is drinking water or eating aquatic plants, but the processes of infection actually have never been observed.

Apparently, after being ingested the larvae penetrate through the digestive tract of the host, as the remainder of development takes place in the insect's body cavity. After considerable growth has been accomplished, the larvae undergo a mild sort of metamorphosis to attain the adult condition. During transition such structures as the proboscis, for example, gradually degenerate, while the intestine elongates, and the gonads and nervous system develop. Only during heavy rain or when the host is near water do the fully grown juveniles leave the host. After molting, the new adults live in either mud or water for a short free existence.

### V. THE ROTIFERA

Animal specializations for immensity of size, like those shown by whales, elephants, and dinosaurs, although amazing, are nonetheless readily perceived to be extremely useful. What is difficult to comprehend is a reason for any multicellular organism assuming such microscopic dimensions as the 2,000 species of rotifers have. Yet such an adaptation must have its advantages, to judge from the frequency with which these animals occur. But striking as the reduction in size may be, there are other developments in this group that are at least as spectacular.

*Morphology*

About the size of *Paramecium,* average rotifers resemble that ciliate also in having a number of cilia, but the bristles in these animals are concentrated around one end in the form of a *corona* (Fig. 43). Often the corona, which is Latin for "crown," is more like a funnel than a head-piece and eventually leads into the mouth. The latter in turn opens into another unusual adaptation, a pharynx or *mastax,* in which several mova-

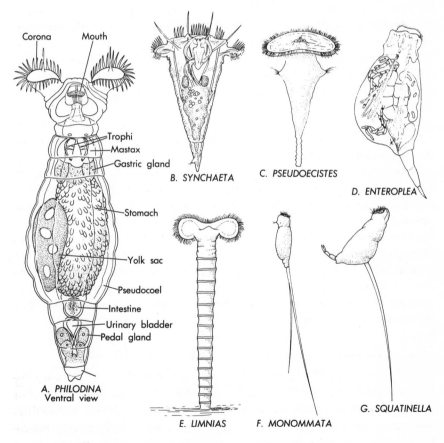

**Fig. 43.** *Structure of rotifers and some diversified representatives.*

ble parts serve as jaws. In action these structures, referred to as *trophi,* look more like rotating choppers and wheels than jaws, but serve the same end, that of grinding the food. Since the diet consists of bacteria and bits of organic matter, the need for grinding is not immediately apparent, until the size of the rotifer itself is considered.

As in the nematodes the body wall is largely epidermal, internally possessing similar scattered muscle fibers and bundles and externally covered by a tough cuticle. Frequently the body may be subdivided into rings that, by telescoping into one another, permit more flexibility than would otherwise be possible in a rigid cuticle. The body cavity is a pseudocoel, while the excretory system consists of a pair of long convoluted collecting tubules and from four to fifty flame cells. The tubules, placed one on each side of the body, lead into a urinary bladder which opens into the cloaca. By and large the nervous system includes a large brain located dorsad to the mastax and several pairs of fine nerve cords which extend to various parts of the body wall. Among the simple sense organs are a eyespot on the brain, a single (rarely paired) antenna dorsally on the "head," and scattered papillae or sensory hairs, depending on the species.

### Habits

By far the majority of the known species are fresh-water inhabitants, fewer than 100 occurring in marine or brackish water. In lakes they may be found anywhere from the surface to the greatest depths. No puddle, not even the water between the particles on moist sandy beaches, is too small to harbor a few of these animals. Masses of damp vegetation, especially mosses, are favored habitants of certain species. Most rotifers are free living, some being active swimmers while others are sessile and often provided with a vaselike envelope, or lorica. A number of symbiotic varieties are known, however; of these the majority are commensals, living externally on such fresh-water invertebrates as insects and crustaceans. Others, like *Albertia,* are either ectoparasites or endoparasites of aquatic earthworms and similar invertebrates, whereas certain members of the phylum parasitize various algae. For example, *Proales parasitica* occurs quite commonly in the cavities of *Volvox* colonies.

Rotifers of the order Bdelloidea that inhabit mosses have a peculiar diversification. Because their habitat is frequently subjected to protracted periods of drought, these organisms have acquired an ability to undergo desiccation. Without forming a cyst, under severe conditions the body loses water and becomes quite shrunken and spherical. The pseudocoel nearly disappears as the body is reduced to less than one-third of its normal size. Even the chromatin matter of the individual cells undergoes changes; instead of remaining as a mass centrally in each nucleus, it breaks into fragments that move to the inner surface of the cell membrane. Thus desiccated, rotifers can remain dry as dust for a considerable period, more than twenty-five years in one recorded case. When these desiccated specimens happen to reach water, they rapidly absorb moisture and resume normal activity; recovery time may involve a period as long as a full day or as short as ten minutes, depending on the species and circumstances.

### Reproduction

Almost without exception the rotifers studied in the laboratory are of one sex, female! Male rotifers are known for but a handful of species, and these generally occur only during a definite period of the year. None of this sex ever live for more than three days, for, lacking a mouth and anus and frequently most of the rest of the digestive tract, they are unable to feed. As a rule they are much smaller than the corresponding female and are active swimmers, even in those species in which the females are sessile. Especially in those forms that inhabit temporary ponds, males are found only near the close of the summer; after fertilizing the eggs, they live a couple of days and disappear until the same time the following year. Yet the appearance of members of this sex, brief though it may be, is essential to the survival of the species over winter, for only fertilized eggs are resistant to cold.

The mechanism that controls this sudden appearance and absence of males involves the production by the females of two kinds of eggs, *mictic* and *amictic*. The first of these is produced by meiosis and is haploid like most eggs, whereas the second is formed without reduction in chromosome number and is therefore diploid. Moreover, the eggs differ in hatching requirements and in shell characteristics. Amictic, or summer, eggs hatch within a day or two after being deposited and have only a thin shell, if any; whereas mictic eggs, which are of two types, have a thicker one. Unfertilized mictic eggs, with a moderately heavy shell, hatch within two or three days into males. In contrast, fertilized ones are thick-shelled and remarkably resistant to freezing, drying, and other adverse conditions; they uniformly require a resting period of several weeks or months before hatching into females.

In brief, a typical life cycle might commence with the thawing of the pond ice in spring, when the overwintering resting eggs hatch into amictic females. As the name implies these females lay amictic eggs, which hatch into similar females. After twenty to forty of such amictic generations, depending upon the species and climate, when the pond waters undergo a slight cooling a number of females produce eggs meiotically (Fig. 44). All the mictic eggs first produced, being unfertilized,

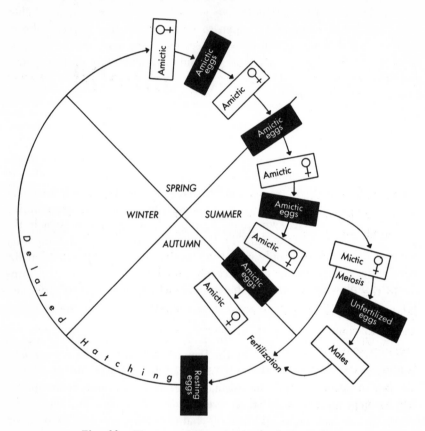

**Fig. 44.** *The annual reproductive cycle in rotifers.*

within a few days hatch into males. Thereafter many mictic eggs are fertilized, and these resting eggs remain unhatched until the following spring. But until the waters become too cold, additional generations of amictic females may be produced as during the summer months.

# CHAPTER 9

# The annelid line

At the top of the metazoan evolutionary tree are two major branches, each of which possesses a true coelom. Since both lines of development are highly successful, as evidenced by their including the predominant animals of the land as well as the seas, they suggest the extensive diversity the advent of that cavity made possible.

In the stem to be discussed first, that which begins with the Annelida, a second body characteristic, *segmentation*, puts in an early appearance and continues throughout the entire line. Perhaps this trait, too, provides some basis for the success of these animals, as greater diversification occurs here than anywhere else in the zoological world. But the number of species found along this branch is part of another story and will be held until later.

## I. THE ANNELIDA

Since wormlike forms have dominated much of the earlier history of the metazoans, it is not at all surprising that this branch should have its origin in a phylum of similar habit. The present worms are distinguished by their being the last such creatures to become highly successful as indicated by their fairly large representation. Although one or two phyla of a creeping nature will be discussed later, few species among these groups survive today.

### Characteristics

While the principal traits of the phylum are made sufficiently clear by the diagram (Fig. 45), several require brief discussion. The circulatory system is of the closed variety, resembling that of the nemertineans in having both arteries and veins. Sometimes the blood is red, as it contains hemoglobin similar to that found in human blood corpuscles; in

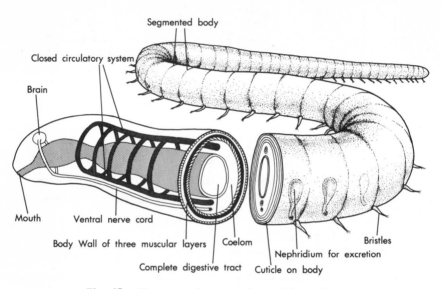

**Fig. 45.** *The major features of annelid morphology.*

the annelids, however, it is carried in the plasma, not in the blood cells. In most representatives the coelom is divided into small chambers by cross-walls, called *septa,* located between the segments. While the digestive tract is often complex, the extent of its development varies widely from group to group.

The distinguishing features of the classes are summarized in Table 7.

### A. The Polychaeta

### Habits

The class Polychaeta includes marine worms whose mode of life is extremely varied. Certain of its members, the *errant* polychaetes, are especially adapted for actively creeping along the sea bottoms. The well-marked head is provided with a protrusible pharynx usually equipped

TABLE 7

*The Classes of Annelida*

| Characteristic | Classes | | | |
| --- | --- | --- | --- | --- |
| | Archiannelida | Polychaeta | Oligochaeta | Hirudinea |
| Segments | Few, poorly indicated | Sharply marked internally and externally | Sharply marked internally and externally | Well marked internally only |
| Clitellum | Absent | Absent | Present | Present |
| Setae | Usually absent | Numerous, borne on parapodia | Several rows, on body | Absent |
| Suckers | Absent | Absent | Absent | Present |
| Head | Distinct, with appendages | Distinct, with appendages | Absent | Absent |
| Sexes | Separate | Separate | United | United |
| Larva | Trochophore | Trochophore | Absent | Absent |
| Habitat | Marine | Marine | Fresh-water and terrestrial | Marine, fresh-water, and terrestrial |
| Common names | None | Clamworms, sandworms, etc. | Earthworms, limnicolous worms | Leeches |

with a pair of strong jaws with which they attack clams and other invertebrates. Although they frequently burrow into the sea bottom, they have no special adaptations for that type of existence. In contrast, the *burrowing* type is adapted for a subterranean life, particularly through the reduction of certain parts. For forming burrows through the ocean floor in earthworm fashion, such genera as *Arenicola* have the head inconspicuous and the pharynx short and unarmed. The *tubiculous* polychaetes, the most highly diversified forms, spend their entire adult lives in tubes. Specializations within this group are often very complex and striking, the tentacles especially being highly developed. In *Sabella* (Fig. 46), for instance, fifteen to twenty of these organs are present, all of which are plumelike and perhaps two-thirds as long as the body. When feeding, the worm remains within its tube, the tentacles projecting into the sea water. Here the cilia with which these organs are clothed set up currents, sweeping small particles inward to be captured in the tentacles' longitudinal grooves. Along these, the particles are conducted toward the mouth but before entering pass through a sievelike chamber. Only the smallest particles drop into the mouth, while medium-sized ones are directed into the worm's tube for use in construction, and overly large ones are returned to the sea.

The body, too, may be highly adapted for this way of life. In most tubiculous species the segments gradually diminish in size posteriorly, so that the body is conical rather than cylindrical as in typical worms. Often a separate head, thorax, and abdomen are recognizable, as exemplified by *Sabella*, the genus mentioned above.

But the greatest specialization probably is found in *Chaetopterus*, a form that dwells in U-shaped tubes in the sea bottoms. While the characteristic tentacles of many other tube-dwellers are here reduced, there is a broad collar around the head with a tentacle-like fringe along the dorsal opening (Fig. 46), and, just posterior to that, a pair of winglike parapodia bear a series of mucous glands. These glands secrete a bag that serves in filtering food particles from the sea water. It is so arranged that the particles collect in a cuplike elevation to be formed into small balls and passed forward to the mouth. Along the entire ventral surface of the thorax, the parapodia are modified as suction disks to secure the worm in its burrow, while dorsally three broad sets are specialized as fans. These beat rhythmically to circulate water through the tube and bring in food and dissolved oxygen. Behind them the tapering abdomen consists of segments lacking distinctive adaptations.

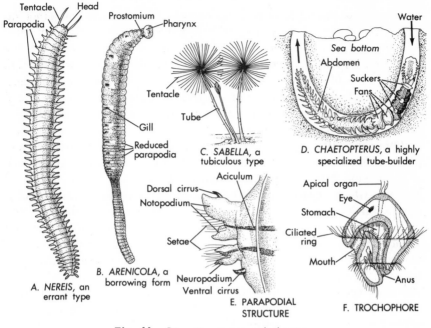

**Fig. 46.** *Diversity among polychaetes.*

*Reproduction*

In many polychaetes the gonads are merely specialized areas of the epithelial lining of the coelom, situated in most of the segments. The sperm or eggs they produce are deposited directly into the body cavity, where they collect in large numbers, sometimes entirely filling the segment. After undergoing maturation, the gametes leave the coelom either by way of the nephridial tubules or by rupturing the body wall.

Since the sexes are separate in the polychaetes, swarming is of frequent occurrence during the period of gamete release. When sexually mature, the worms, whether active bottom-dwellers or tube-formers, rise to the surface and swim about vigorously; then, after the gametes have been released, all return to the bottom once more. Not infrequently, soon after discharging the sex cells, the reproducing individuals perish.

Many adaptations for bringing the sexes together at swarming time have been acquired. Among errant types the parapodia frequently undergo radical changes as the sex organs mature; *Nereis* and its relatives become so modified that the sexual form is given the distinctive name *heteronereis*. As sexual maturity approaches in this genus, the body musculature breaks down and is consumed by leukocytes before new muscles of a different form begin growth. In the meantime the parapodia become modified by increasing in length, their several lobes enlarging into membranous frills. At the same time the old setae are lost, to be replaced with flattened ones that appear like so many oars. Moreover, the eyes increase greatly in size and the entire body of the worm becomes sensitive to light. While some of these developments doubtlessly are of value in swimming and floating, other enhance the efficiency of the gills for the very active mating period.

Other examples of diversity for reproductive purposes are provided by the palolo worm and others of the genus *Leodice.* In these inhabitants of coral reefs the entire posterior half of the worm becomes filled with gametes, which ripen at a specific time of the year. In the West Indian species breeding occurs only during the third quarter of the June-July moon. Then the posterior half of the worm breaks off and rises to the surface, writhing actively, and discharges its contents into the sea. Often the worms are so abundant that the waters become turbid with released gametes. The palolo worm of the South Pacific behaves similarly but is still more specific as to the time of swarming. This takes place only at moonrise on that night during the latter half of October or early November when the moon attains its last quarter.

Among most polychaetes, the fertilized egg develops into a peculiar larva called the *trochophore* or *trochosphere.* In many ways the trochophore superficially resembles the pilidium of the ribbonworms, especially in having an apical organ at one pole. Instead of being ciliated over the entire surface, however, the present larva bears a band of cilia around its middle, and its digestive tract is of the complete type (Fig. 46). Because it is found also in several other phyla to be described later, the trochophore is of great biological importance in suggesting relationships between otherwise quite dissimilar groups.

### B. The Oligochaeta

Many features of the polychaetes are absent in the present class, including the parapodia, protrusible pharynx, distinct head, and palpi. On the other hand, the reproductive system among the oligochaetes is better developed, as is also the circulatory system. Two major types are included, the terrestrial earthworms and aquatic limicolous members.

*Morphology*

The main features of anatomy are made clear by the illustration (Fig. 47), but a few points require comment. The *clitellum* is an organ of secretion found elsewhere only in the leeches. Although in large earthworms it is present throughout life, in the majority of species it becomes evident only with the approach of the breeding season, during which it plays two important roles (see below).

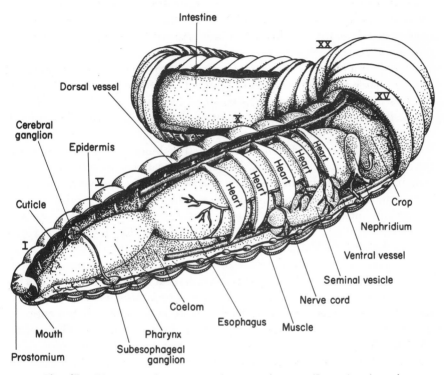

**Fig. 47.** *The internal anatomy of an earthworm.* (Reproduced, with permission, from L. S. Dillon, *Principles of Animal Biology,* New York: The Macmillan Company, copyright 1965.)

Externally the setae, usually eight per segment, are borne directly on the body wall, where they form rows along the ventral and lateral surfaces. A prolongation over the mouth, known as the *prostomium,* alone distinguishes the anterior end from the posterior, for no eyes or tentacles are present.

### The Nervous System

In all annelids the nervous system consists basically of a ventral nerve cord enlarged in each segment to form a ganglion. In addition there is a brain (prostomial ganglia) to which a pair of subesophageal ganglia are connected by means of a commissure on each side of the pharynx. On a functional basis the organization into two separate reflex systems is a distinctive feature. One set, the *intrasegmental reflexes,* coordinates the contraction of the muscles which compose the wall of each segment. Here two types of muscles oppose each other, the longitudinal muscles reducing the length of the segment whereas the circular ones cause elongation. The reflexes are organized so that when one set of muscles has been induced to contract the other is caused to relax. The second system, the *intersegmental reflexes,* coordinates the activities of corresponding muscles in adjacent segments. For example, if the circular muscles in segment 10 should be induced to contract by intrasegmental fibers, those in segment 11 are made to follow suit, followed by those in segment 12 and on to the end of the body through the activities of the intersegmental nerves. In the meantime the longitudinal muscles may have been activated in segment 10, so a correlated wave of contraction is initiated throughout the body. By use of the intra- and intersegmental reflex in this alternating fashion, the normal mode of locomotion is brought about.

In addition to the short nerve fibers that comprise the reflexes, typically a system of *giant fibers* runs the entire length of the body. These fibers enable the whole organism to be brought under the control of the higher centers, the brain and the subesophageal ganglia. If these centers are strongly excited, as when the worm's anterior is grasped by fingers or a bird's beak, all of the longitudinal muscles are induced to contract. The brain has the additional function of inhibiting reflexes. If that organ of a live earthworm is removed, the animal moves about constantly, for nothing now suppresses the intra- and intersegmental reflexes. If both higher centers are removed, the animal becomes permanently quiescent, for nothing now excites the segmental reflexes into action.

### Reproduction

As oligochaetes are hermaphroditic, the reproductive organs typically include one pair of testes each in segments 10 and 11 and a pair of ovaries in segment 13. The ducts which carry the gametes have funnel-like openings internally, located just behind the gonads. The external openings of the oviducts are on the segment that immediately follows the ovaries, while those of the sperm ducts extend posteriorly as far as segments 15 or 16. As a rule the testes are enclosed in saclike *seminal vesicles* in which sperm are stored until ready for release. In addition, one or two pairs of *sperm receptacles* are found in the segment or segments preceding those that bear the testes.

Mating in *Lumbricus* and other large earthworms involves mutual insemination. The worms lie with ventral surfaces in contact, each with segments 9 and 10 adjacent to the clitellum of the other. The clitella then secretes mucous tubes over the anterior ends of the worms, while the sperm pass out through the openings of the sperm ducts to flow along seminal grooves on the ventral surface to the clitellum. How the sperm are conducted from this organ to the sperm receptacles for storage has never been established.

Some days after mating oviposition takes place. The clitellum secretes a mucous tube over the anterior end as during copulation but this time to serve as a cocoon. As the tube moves forward over the body, eggs are deposited in it along with an albuminous secretion; further cephalad, in passing over the seminal receptacles, the eggs are fertilized. Finally, a series of strong contractions frees the cocoon, which remains in the ground while the eggs develop. After hatching, the young feed upon the albuminous material until they undergo a series of mild changes and emerge.

## C. The Hirudinea

Unlike the Oligochaeta in which the number of segments varies both with the age of the individual and from species to species, thirty-two segments plus a prostomium are uniformly present in the leeches that comprise the Hirudinea, the present class. As the segments externally are subdivided into a series of rings or *annuli,* the actual number is apparent only inside the body. Leeches differ from earthworms also in lacking setae and in possessiong one sucker at each end of the body. Depending on the family, jaws or a protrusible pharynx may be present.

Kinship with the Oligochaeta is indicated by several shared traits, particularly by the present of a clitellum during the breeding season. The gland functions in the same fashion here as in the preceding group, secreting tubes during mating and a cocoon for the development of the young. In the embryogeny, too, certain technical features are identical in the two taxa, as are also the excretory and reproductive systems. Because of these likenesses and such others as the sexes being united, many European zoologists place the two groups in a class named the Clitellata.

### Habits

While the vast majority of the leeches live in fresh waters, a number are marine, and a few, particularly in the Old World, are terrestrial. In water most species are skillful swimmers; on dry land or mud they progress by a series of loops, much like those of a "measuring-worm," using the suckers to provide positive traction.

Food habits are quite varied. A number of leeches feed upon decaying flesh and are therefore scavengers, while a relatively few prey upon small animals, such as earthworms, snails, and insect larvae. Several are parasites in a strict sense, but the majority are notorious for their bloodsucking habits. For the latter mode of feeding a number of specializations have been developed. In gathering the fluid food, an anticoagulant is a necessity and is found abundantly in the saliva of such genera as *Hirudo,* the medicinal leech. Since prey of the proper kind may be encountered only occasionally, a provision has been acquired that permits large blood meals to be consumed at one time, often to the extent of several times the worm's own weight. This feat is accomplished by means of the large crop and by lateral extensions on that organ called *diverticula.* After a full meal the fluid part of the blood is absorbed into the leech's circulatory system, to be eliminated by the nephridia during the course of several days; in this way the body soon resumes nearly normal proportions. Digestion of the solid remains of the meal then proceeds slowly, as a rule requiring several months for completion.

So far as effects upon man and his economy are concerned, the aquatic species hold only a nuisance value, except for a small number that attack domestic animals. Perhaps the worst of these is the horse leech (*Limnatis nilotica*), a form that lives around the Mediterranean Sea and in the Near East. While the adult feeds harmlessly on worms and small fish, the young often cause consideraable damage. As the minute juveniles spend most of their time in the surface waters of ponds and tanks, they are frequently swallowed by horses, cattle, and even human beings while drinking. In passing through the mouth and throat, they attach themselves to the lining of those organs, occasionally in such numbers that the host dies from loss of blood.

The terrestrial species, particularly of the genus *Haemadipsa,* are undoubtedly the most detrimental. In tropical regions throughout the world, but particularly in rain forests extending from India into Australia, the leeches occur in such large numbers that some areas are uninhabitable by man. In the forests the worms lie relatively inactive on grasses and low bushes until a vertebrate approaches. Then, detecting the host either by the vibration of its movements or by the warmth radiating from its body, they quickly move toward it by looping as described above. A traveler along a jungle trail need pause for only a moment before he finds himself being converged upon by dozens or even hundreds of these leeches.

## II. THE ONYCHOPHORA

One of the diversifications undergone during remote times by ancestral animals would have remained unknown to science were it not for a handful of species still surviving today, for the fossil record is devoid of their presence. How many other soft-bodied groups similarly came and went during geological times without leaving any trace can only be conjectured. In the present group the seventy or so living species occur in such tropical places as the West Indies, Borneo, Malaya, and the Congo, but a few are found in subtropical and temperate areas like New Zealand, Australia, and South Africa. Most frequently they live under the bark of fallen trees and in the litter of forest floors.

As might be expected of an archaic group, *Peripatus* and its allies do not fall readily into any existing phylum and have in bygone days been variously classed as annelids, slugs, and millipedes. Presently they are considered a separate phylum between the Annelida and the Arthropoda and are believed to represent a transitional stage in the latter's origin from the former.

### Morphology

Resemblances to the Annelida are found in the muscular body wall covered by a thin cuticle, the series of segmentally arranged pairs of nephridia, and the numerous legs which are not unlike parapodia in construction (Fig. 48). In contrast to the Annelida, however, the body is not visibly divided into segments, segmentation being indicated externally only by the appendages and internally by the nephridia. Even the nervous system lacks any indication of serially arranged ganglia, consisting largely of a brain and two longitudinal nerve cords. The only sense organs present that are specialized for a single function is the pair of simple eyes. In addition, a pair of tentacles located on the head and several series of papillae on the dorsal surface serve both in touch and chemoreception.

The construction of the nephridia is really more like that of the arthropods than the annelids, for near each tubule's exit there is a bladder derived from the ectoderm, as in the crustacean's green or coxal gland. Also indicative of kinship with the arthropods are the hemocoel and tracheae. The former will be recalled as a special cavity which serves as a part of the circulatory system, while the latter are fine tubes which

**121**

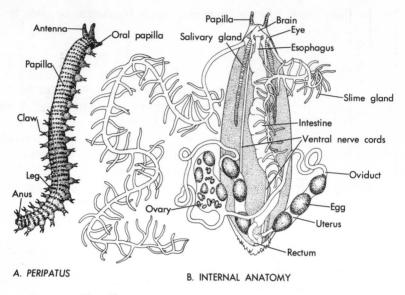

**Fig. 48.** *Peripatus and its internal morphology.*

conduct air from external pores directly to the various body parts. Unlike those of insects, *spiracles*, as the pores are called, cannot be opened and closed; since water-vapor loss thus is uncontrollable, these creatures are confined to moister regions of the globe. It has been found that under similar atmospheric conditions, *Peripatus* loses body moisture twice as rapidly as an earthworm, forty times as fast as a caterpillar, and more than eighty times the rate of a roach!

### III. THE ARTHROPODA

Were all phyla except the present one absent, the Metazoa would still show an astonishing amount of diversification, for a million and more species of Arthropoda are known to exist. These range in body size from microscopic mites to spider crabs 14 feet long. Wormlike, fishlike, and birdlike forms are included, and locomotion may be by creeping, walking, swimming, jumping, sailing, or flying. Defense mechanisms run the gamut from pincers on the legs to biting jaws and poison fangs, and from stingers on the tail to glands that secrete acetic acid and scent, to mention only the more obvious adaptations. Because of the extensive variation, the phylum is divided into a number of classes, the major distinc-

TABLE 8

*The Major Classes of Arthropoda*

| Characteritic | Classes | | | | | |
|---|---|---|---|---|---|---|
| | Crustacea | Diplopoda | Chilopoda | Insecta | Merostomata | Arachnida |
| Antennae | 2 pairs | 1 pair | 1 pair | 1 pair | Absent | Absent |
| Mandibles | Present | Present | Present | Present | Absent | Absent |
| Body divisions | Frequently cephalothorax and abdomen | Head, thorax, and abdomen | Head and body | Head, thorax, and abdomen | Cephalothorax and abdomen | Cephalothorax and abdomen |
| Thoracic appendages | 2 to 11 pairs | 3 pairs | 1 pair per segment | 3 pairs | 5 pairs | 4 pairs |
| Abdominal appendages | Absent or present | 2 pair per segment | 1 pair per segment | Absent | Absent | Absent |
| Respiratory organs | Gills | Tracheae | Tracheae | Tracheae | Book gills | Lung books or tracheae |
| Excretory organs | Coxal glands | Malphigian tubules | Malphigian tubules | Malphigian tubules | Coxal glands | Coxal glands |
| Larva | Nauplius, zoea, and others | 3-legged larva | Absent | Caterpillar, grubs, maggots, etc.; often absent | Absent | Usually absent; mites with 3-legged larva |
| Habitats | Fresh-water, marine, and terrestrial | Terrestrial | Terrestrial | Fresh-water and terrestrial | Marine | Principally terrestrial |
| Common names | Crabs, crayfish, shrimp, sand fleas, water fleas, sow bugs, etc. | Millipedes | Centipedes | Insects: bugs, beetles, moths, butterflies, flies, wasps, lice, etc. | King crab, horseshoe crab | Spiders, mites, ticks, vinegaroons, scorpions |

tions of which are summarized in Table 8, while the characters of the phylum are depicted in Figure 49.

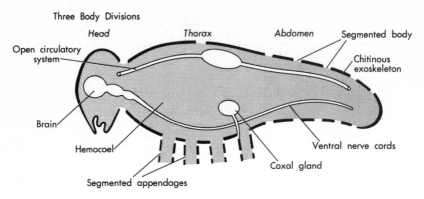

**Fig. 49.** *The distinctive characteristics of the phylum Arthropoda.*

### A. The Crustacea

Although swimming is listed above as a single mode of locomotion, the number of ways in which it is accomplished even within the present class, Crustacea, is quite incredible. Most species swim forward, but the members of one group progress backward more rapidly, and those of another order (Fig. 51) swim upside down! As a result of these and other diversities, the class is divided into six subclasses (Table 9) and eighteen orders.

### The Larger Malacostracans

The 35,000 known members of the class include such familiar large forms as the crabs, lobsters, and crayfish; nearly 10,000 species of these large types occur, largely scattered through the temperate and tropical parts of the world. As the crayfish and lobster are nearly universally studied in the laboratory of introductory courses, little need be said about their morphology (Fig. 50). Most forms with large abdomens are strictly aquatic, but some crayfish are semiaquatic and dig deep burrows in the ground. Each burrow is occupied by a single specimen except during the breeding season and is always constructed in such a way that one portion extends below the water table. The "chimneys" that characterize crayfish burrows appear to serve no particular

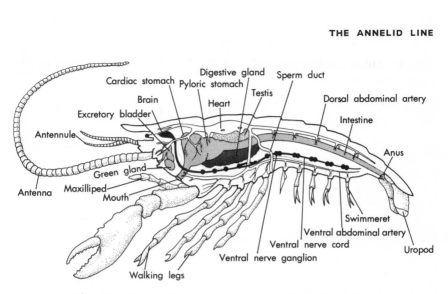

**Fig. 50.** *The anatomy and appendages of the crayfish.*

purpose but consist of mud pellets deposited by the crayfish in constructing the tube.

The crabs are as a group much more highly diversified than the long-abdomened crayfishes and lobsters. In these forms, the "tail" has been reduced to a mere remnant folded around one end of the body. Consequently, the abdomen is of no value in swimming; instead, strictly aquatic forms as the edible types have the walking legs flattened like oars for that purpose. But most crabs do not possess this adaptation and are restricted to terrestrial habitats, occupying burrows along the sea shores by day and actively foraging at night.

### Planktonic Forms

Although the foregoing representatives are the most conspicuous, the majority of Crustacea are forms so minute that they are considered a part of the *plankton,* or floating life, of lakes and seas in spite of their well-developed appendages. In both fresh-water and marine habitats, the members of this group play roles of extreme importance in being intermediaries betwen the microscopic protozoa and bacteria on which they feed and the fish which prey upon them. Some of the more important types are shown in Figure 51.

### Cave-Dwelling Crustacea

In the central portion of the United States, extending from the southern Alleghenies through Indiana to eastern Kansas and southward

TABLE 9

*The Subclasses of Crustacea*

| Characteristic | Subclass | | | | | |
|---|---|---|---|---|---|---|
| | Branchiopoda | Ostracoda | Copepoda | Branchiura | Cirripedia | Malacostraca |
| Carapace | Covers thorax, sometimes head and limbs too; occasionally absent | Bivalvular | Absent | Formed from head, not thorax | Encloses much of body | Covers thorax, sometimes absent |
| Eyes | Compound, sessile or stalked | Simple or compound | Simple | Compound | Simple in adult | Compound, stalked |
| Thorax | 9-11 segments | 2 segments | 7 segments | 5 segments | 7 segment or less | 8 segments |
| Thoracic limbs | 5-11 pairs, usually broad and lobed, strongly bristled | 2 pairs | 6 pairs | 4 pairs | 6 pairs or fewer | 8 pairs |
| Abdominal appendages | Sometimes present on basal segments, always absent on at least 3 apical segments | Absent | Absent | Absent | Absent | 6 pairs |
| Habits | Free-living, mostly fresh-water | Free-living | Free-living or parasitic | Temporary parasites on fish | Free-living and sessile, or parasitic | Free-living |
| Common name | Fairy shrimp, brine-shrimp, water fleas | Seed shrimp | ——— | Fish lice | Barnacles | Crabs, crayfish, lobsters, amphipods, isopods |

into east Texas is a great belt of caves, most of which contain streams and pools. Moreover, the streams frequently continue along low underground passageways many miles from actual caverns. In these subterranean waters are many species of Crustacea which have become especially adapted to the conditions of continual darkness. Often all pigmentation has been lost so that the integument is white or straw-colored. While the eyes are usually vestigal or absent, antennae are well-developed, as are also sensory hairs. Even forms as large as crayfish are specialized for this mode of life, but the cave-dwelling species do not generally become as large as above-ground inhabitants, about 3 inches being the maximum length.

Nearly all the subterranean forms in North America belong to the Malacostraca, including isopods, amphipods, and crayfish, but in Europe a number of copepods have also been described from such habitats. The majority live within caves, but springs which open on the surface nearby are also frequently occupied. Occasionally isopods and amphipods are reported from wells many miles from any known cave. Their food, besides an occasional piece of vegetation that may be washed into

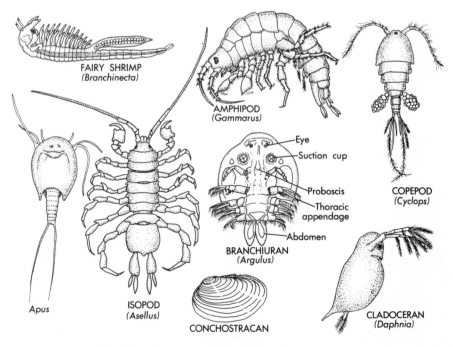

**Fig. 51.** *Diversity among planktonic crustaceans.*

cave waters, consists of the fine surface-scum of bacteria that coats underground rocks and soil particles.

### Parasitic Species

Among any animal group probably the most bizarre are parasitic crustaceans of the subclasses Copepoda and Cirripedia. Indeed, some are so highly differentiated from their relatives that they can be placed as members of the group only through the free-living larval stage. The

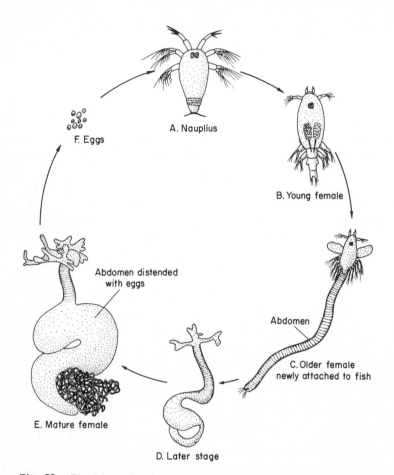

F. Eggs

A. Nauplius

B. Young female

Abdomen distended
with eggs

Abdomen

C. Older female
newly attached to fish

E. Mature female

D. Later stage

**Fig. 52.** *The life cycle of a parasitic copepod.* Many parasitic species are so highly diversified that they are recognizable as crustaceans only by the nauplius larva that also characterizes other less specialized types. (Reproduced, with permission, from L. S. Dillon, *Principles of Animal Biology*, New York: The Macmillan Company, copyright 1965.)

newly hatched larva shows few striking characteristics but, soon after attachment to the host, loses appendages and frequently segmentation also (Fig. 52) in developing into the adult. Consequently, mature specimens appear like so many sacs or, at best, lice, rather than typical crustaceans. Fresh-water and marine fish are the chief hosts, on which the parasites occupy the skin, fins, or gills; some of the parasitic barnacles, however, use crayfish and crabs as the host.

## B. The So-Called Myriapoda

Two types of Arthropoda are so similar in general body morphology that for many years zoologists combined them in a single taxon called the "myriapods." But, while the two share such features as a wormlike body and a multitude of legs upon the abdomen, they are so distinct in other ways that today they are more usually treated as separate classes.

### Class Diplopoda

*Millipedes,* as the members of this class are called, are cylindrical forms, usually rather slender, with bodies no thicker than a pencil even when 5 or 6 inches long (Fig. 53). Their chief distinction is in the number of legs present. While the thorax bears only one pair of legs on each of its three segments, all twenty or more abdominal segments possess two pairs each. However, because the legs are short and weak, the animals can move only at a snail's pace at best.

Damp situations, including old cellars, moist woodland debris, old corn shocks, and well-decayed logs are the millipedes' favored habitats, while the diet includes fungal and fern spores, yeasts, and bits of half-decayed vegetation. As in all terrestrial arthropods, fertilization of the eggs takes place within the female's body. From the egg a minute three-legged larva hatches which looks more like an insect than a millipede. With each molt, it gains abdominal legs, two or more pairs at a time, until the full adult complement has been acquired.

### The Chilopoda

In contrast to the above, the *centipedes* that constitute the class Chilopoda have fewer but much more efficient appendages. As all segments are alike and similarly provided with a single pair of legs, no subdivision of the body into thorax and abdomen is possible. The head is well differentiated, however, and resembles that of the Diplopoda except in possessing better developed antennae (Fig. 53).

**129**

A peculiar adaptation is found in the first pair of body appendages. Instead of being legs like the remainder, these two, strong, hollow, and pincer-like in construction, extend forward below the mouth parts to serve as poison claws in killing the prey. As a whole the food consists of live insects, especially flies, mosquitoes, and other soft-bodied forms, in the capture of which the speed provided by their strong legs is an important factor.

No distinct larva exists. Upon hatching, the young possess seven body segments, each bearing a single pair of appendages as in the mature forms. With each molt a new segment is added until the full number has been acquired.

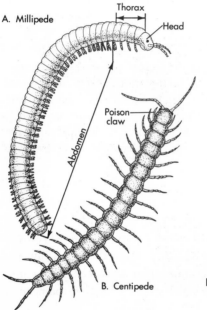

**Fig. 53.** *Millipedes and centipedes.*

## C. The Insecta

Since the class Insecta contains no fewer than one million described species and probably many times that number still undescribed, very little more need be said to demonstrate the vast diversity that exists within it. At least a few representatives are found in every conceivable ecological situation, although the seas are virtually uninhabited by its members. In achieving the diversity in species number and breadth of distribution, specializations have been acquired in the life cycles, mouth parts, and wing structure to such an extent that as many as thirty-five orders are frequently recognized by insect taxonomists. Representatives of a few of these are illustrated in Figure 54.

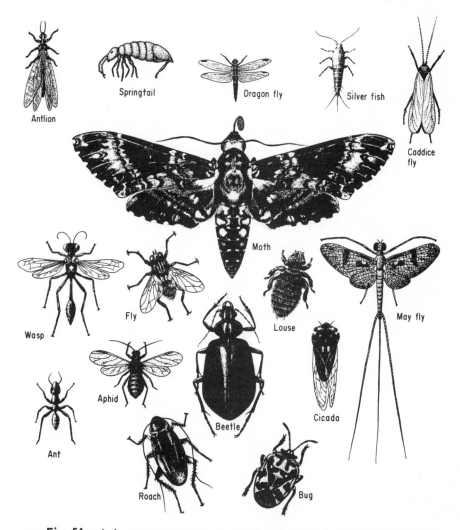

**Fig. 54.** *A few representatives of the class Insecta.* Diversification in this class has been so extensive that many pages would be required to illustrate just the major types. (Reproduced, with permission, from L. S. Dillon, *The Science of Life*, New York: The Macmillan Company, copyright 1964.)

In spite of this diversity, the insects collectively form a well-marked group. Among the distinctive features (Fig. 55) are a numbered shared only with the Chilopoda and Diplopoda, such as the single pair of antennae and true Malpighian tubules. The latter are elongate tubes attached to the digestive tract which eliminate nitrogeneous wastes by converting them into uric acid crystals. In number they range from four to a hundred or more but are completely absent in the group known as

Three body divisions:

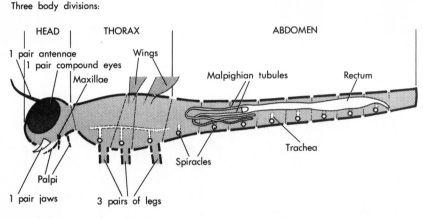

**Fig. 55.** *The distinctive features of insects.*

plant lice. While so-called Malpighian tubules occur also in the Arachnida, in that group their excretory nature has never been clearly demonstrated; consequently, they are not generally considered homologous to those of the three classes mentioned.

Because whole books would be required to discuss in detail the specializations of the various orders, only a few samples will be provided. These selections, it is hoped, will enable the student to discover for himself that, striking though the morphological differences may be between a beetle and a butterfly or a grasshopper and an ant, far greater but less apparent ones exist in insect internal functionings.[1]

---

[1]For additional examples refer to K. von Frisch, "Dialects in the Language of the Bees," *Scientific American,* August, 1962: C. G. Johnson, "The Aerial Migration of Insects," *ibid.,* December, 1963: D. S. Smith, "The Flight Muscles of Insects," *ibid.,* June, 1965; M. Rothschild, "Fleas," *ibid.,* December, 1965; P. Villiard, "Multicolored World of Caterpillars," *Natural History* 73(4):24-31, April, 1964.

*Diversification in Feeding Habits*

Under this heading, the discussion could logically be devoted to the numerous specializations to which the mouth parts have been subjected. But highly modified though these are, the methods of treating the foods after being secured and swallowed show even more numerous diversifications.

As in human beings and other vertebrates, foods are digested principally by enzymatic action and, in such omnivorous forms as the roaches, series of enzymes similary break down proteins (proteases), fats (lipases), carbohydrates (carbohydrases), or nucleic acids (nucleases). Insects adapted to a special diet often show a deficiency of one or more types of enzymes. In tsetse flies, which feed on blood, all carbohydrases are absent, whereas among adult blowflies, whose food is rich in carbohydrates, most of the proteases as well as the lipases are lacking. Sometimes this type of diversity is carried to the greatest degree, as among leaf-mining caterpillars. These extremely small and flat caterpillars spend their entire life within the interior of a leaf, feeding upon a single region of cells. In some cases, a species may feed upon the upper or columnar layer of leaf cells, while others consume only the lower or spongy layer. If by chance the egg of one such species is deposited in the wrong layer of the leaf, the caterpillar soon perishes because it lacks the enzymes necessary to digest the proteins of those cells.

Many insects burrow through trees or feed on plant tissues, but few are actually able themselves to utilize the cellulose of the tissues. The larvae of cerambycid (long-horned) beetles are among the exceptions that possess the necessary specialized enzymes. On the other hand, plant-eating caterpillars cannot utilize cellulose but have enzymes which penetrate the cell walls and digest the protoplasm within. In other wood-eating insects, such as termites, certain woodroaches, and death-watch beetle larvae, symbiotic organisms in the intestine carry out the actual digestion of cellulose, a fact already pointed out in the discussion of certain protozoa. Still others, like the beetles that drill extensive burrows beneath bark, do not in reality feed upon the wood but eat the fungi which grow in the tunnels.

In a number of groups the saliva serves both in digesting and ingesting food. For example, among the larvae of tiger beetles and flesh-flies, the protease-rich saliva is poured out upon the prey and then lapped up after the proteins have been digested. Consequently these insects thus depend upon external digestion to a large degree. Bees, which feed mainly upon nectar and pollen, are so highly specialized that they have four types of salivary glands. The secretion of some of these attacks nectar, and that of others, pollen, while the remainder add formic acid, apparently to prevent spoilage of the foods during storage in the honeycombs.

### Specializations for Escape

Undoubtedly the elementary and secondary schools have already supplied a familiarity with insect adaptations which assist in escaping attack of predators. Such things, then, as bodies that imitate plant spines or bird droppings, scent glands that secrete a repellant, or wings that resemble leaves need not receive attention. Here mention will be made only of two adaptations of night-flying insects which seem to be of particular value in defense against nocturnal insect-eating mammals and birds.

The first of these, the production of light by fireflies, apparently serves to some degree for recognition purposes and for sexual attraction, but its major value may be an indirect one in defense. When fireflies are fed to a young insect-eating bird, for example, on the first occasion they are usually quickly rejected and thereafter steadfastly refused — facts suggesting that the beetles possess an unpleasant taste. While such a repugnant quality might provide ample protection to an insect against day-feeding insectivorous vertebrates, who quickly learn to discriminate between edible and inedible forms, it can be of little value to a nocturnal species unless some other device enables its predators to recognize it before capture. Among the fireflies the flashing light provides such a recognition character, so that night-feeding birds and bats avoid attacking these insects.[2]

The second example is a peculiar defense mechanism of moths against the unusual method of food-locating employed by the bats. As the student may know, these mammals, while flying at night, emit extremely high-pitched sound waves, the echoes of which they detect with their sensitive ears, in this fashion avoiding obstacles and locating their food of flying insects. Recent experiments by F. A. Webster and others have shown that bats actually can plot the course of a steadily flying object and intercept it, so that feeding on insects is a fairly routine procedure. However, against this subtle "sonar," one family of moths has acquired an effective means of defense in the form of well-developed ears that detect the bat's

---

[2]For a summary of the current knowledge of bioluminescence, reference can be made to the following: E. N. Harvey, *Bioluminescence,* New York: Academic Press, 1952; W. D. McElroy and H. H. Seliger, "Biological Luminescence," *Scientific American,* December, 1962.

sound waves. K. R. Roeder, A. E. Treat, and others are presently experimenting upon these insects using high-speed cinematography in conjunction with a floodlight and tape recordings of bat calls. They have found that upon exposure to the sounds, some moths immediately respond by an angular change in direction of flight and others by flying in bewildering circles, but the majority react by making a power dive into the grass or shrubbery.[3]

### D. The Arachnida and Relatives

*Morphology*

In the Arachnida and related classes are a number of most unusual features that clearly indicate close relationships. Outstanding among the unique traits is the absence of such important appendages as jaws and antennae. In place of antennae two peculiar types of appendages called chelicerae and pedipalps (Fig. 56) are present. Both are so diversely specialized that generalizations regarding function and morphology are difficult to make. *Chelicerae,* which term figuratively means "claw-antennae," frequently are, as suggested by the translation, pincer-bearing appendages situated anteriorly as antennae are in other arthropods. In

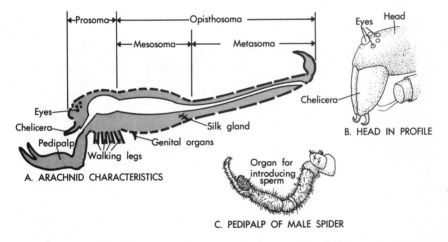

**Fig. 56.** *Some of the characteristics of arachnids.*

---

[3]D. R. Griffin, *Listening in the Dark,* New Haven, Conn.: Yale University Press, 1958, describes in detail the remarkable ability of bats, while K. D. Roeder and A. E. Treat, "The Detection and Evasion of Bats by Moths," *American Scientist* 49:135-148, 1961, relate the equally remarkable reaction of moths.

the spiders, however, these appendages lack claws but bear a hollow spine, through which poison is injected into their prey. *Pedipalpi* are generally longer and more prominent than chelicerae, except among sea-spiders (Pycnogonida) in which the opposite condition prevails. In certain groups like the scorpions and pseudoscorpions, these appendages are provided with pincers, but in spiders they are unarmed. All spiders employ the organ for sensory purposes, but during mating males use them also to introduce the sperm into the female genital tract (Fig. 56).

The division of the body into regions is distinctive too. Although frequently as a matter of convenience (Table 9) a cephalothorax is said to be present, more strictly the first six segments are called the *fore-body* (prosoma), while the remainder is referred to as the *hind-body* (opisthosoma). In turn, the latter may be subdivided into a thick basal part (mesosoma) and a tail-like extension (metasoma).

### Diversity among Arachnida

Though major diversifications made within the arachnoid classes are readily indicated (Fig. 57), the wide range of specialization within the several orders cannot even be intimated.[4] To suggest what possibly has occurred in these — but, of course, along different lines in each case — the food-procuring habits of spiders will be outlined briefly.

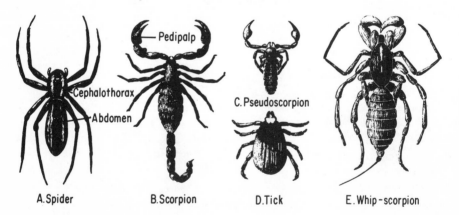

A. Spider      B. Scorpion      D. Tick      E. Whip-scorpion

**Fig. 57.** *Major patterns of diversity among the arachnoids.* (Reproduced, with permission, from L. S. Dillon, *The Science of Life,* New York: The Macmillan Company, copyright 1964.)

---

[4]For specializations that have occurred in another order, read T. H. Savory, "Daddy Long Legs," *Scientific American,* October, 1962; S. Radinovsky, "Mites on a Substrate," *Natural History* 75(6):38-43, June, 1966; or T. Eisner, "Survival by Acid Defense," *ibid.* 71(6):10-19, June, 1962.

The most primitive methods are undoubtedly those of the wolf spiders and related forms which catch terrestrial insects by sheer strength and speed. Some of the larger species, especially in tropical and subtropical regions, are strong and fast enough to capture birds or mammals. While silk glands are present, all are of one variety and are employed solely in wrapping the eggs into a "cocoon." Jumping spiders, while feeding in much the same fashion, are more highly specialized and are more at home on vertical walls than on the bare ground. To assist in holding fast to upright surfaces, their tarsi are provided with an adhesive tuft of hairs; the spider, moreover, uses an additional type of silk gland to spin a strand which trails behind it much as the rope of mountain climbers. The two anterior pairs of eyes, too, are especially adapted to assist in leaping accurately, for a complex series of muscles is present that moves the eyes and directs them toward the intended victim.

Among still more advanced spiders, even greater variety in the silk-producing glands is gradually acquired. Probably the next step in elaborating the use of silk is represented by the trap-door spiders, forms that conceal the entrance to their burrows by trap-doors made of silk and earth. These species, like all that follow, wait for prey to approach, rather than actively foraging as the primitive types do. More advanced forms combine a sheet of silk with the burrow, while still higher ones make a funnel-like tube of silk above ground. Among the latter are the North American black widow and the Australian red-backed spiders, which have an additional adaptation in the form of an especially potent poison. This poison is believed to be, not a defense against vertebrate enemies, but an effective means of quieting their prey, which consist largely of beetles and other active heavy-bodied insects.

The very top of the spider world undoubtedly is represented by the orb-weavers whose intricate web-building habits are too well known to require description here. It can be pointed out, however, that in these forms no fewer than five kinds of silk glands occur. One type, the tubuliform glands employed in making the egg cocoon, is absent from males, while the aciniform set secretes silk for wrapping prey caught in the web. The remainder are used solely in web making. One pair, the pyriform, provides silk to anchor the long radial lines secreted by another set, the ampulliform, while the fifth set, the aggregate, furnishes both the silk for the spiral threads and the viscid fluid which covers them.

# CHAPTER 10

# M ollusks and
## the chordate line

Two major lines of animals exist that have a true coelom as distinctive feature, the one ending in the insects and spiders just described and a second leading to the mammals and birds. In addition there is an important phylum which bears a coelom but whose position relative to these two lines is uncertain. As shall soon be seen, this phylum of doubtful status, the Mollusca, shares a number of traits with the Annelida and undoubtedly should be placed close to that group. But whether it forms an actual branch of the annelid line or is better located close by at the base of the stem leading to the vertebrates are questions that have perplexed zoologists for many years and probably will continue to do so for as many more. It is because of the conflicting points-of-view that this phylum receives attention in this position between the two major lines of evolution.

## I. THE MOLLUSCA

Up to 1957 only five classes of the phylum Mollusca were known to be represented by living forms, but early in that year a Danish zoologist, H. Lemche, reported an exciting mollusk he had just taken off the coast of Costa Rica at depths exceeding 11,000 feet. This species, which he named *Neopilina galatheae,* was the first modern representative ever captured of a class that had previously been known solely from types that lived during Paleozoic times more than 450 million years ago. This member of the class Monoplacophora, then, can be considered a "living fossil" in a very real sense.

*Morphology*

As most of the features which characterize this phylum are readily discerned from the illustration (Fig. 58), only a few remarks are necessary. The body is unsegmented, except in *Neopilina,* where several pairs of hearts, nephridia, and gills show a marked internal segmentation. In all forms the coelom is usually reduced to cavities surrounding the heart

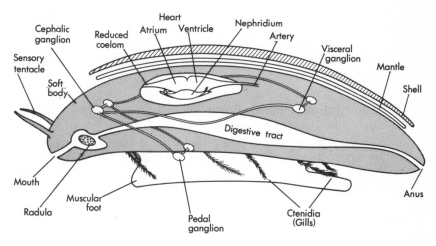

**Fig. 58.** *The principal characteristics of mollusks.*

and gonads, but the precise amount of reduction varies from class to class. Nothing is especially remarkable about the digestive tract except the peculiar organ called the *radula.* This structure consists of a chitinous strap, on one surface of which are numerous fine, horny teeth. In use the radula is moved back and forth by muscles and serves both in obtaining food and in tearing it into small pieces.

The nervous system is unusual in consisting of three pairs of ganglia, often arranged as a triangle. The components of each set are closely interconnected by transverse commissures, while paired major nerve cords connect the ganglia in series. As the cephalic ganglia are no larger than others, they are not considered a brain. The cephalopods are exceptional in this matter, however, for the squids and octopi that comprise the major portions of that class have these ganglia so highly developed that in recent years they have been shown to possess a surprising level of intelligence. In this same group, the eyes are comparable in structure to those of the vertebrates, including man.[1]

### Diversification in the Shell

The shell, secreted by the thin mantle, in general provides the main basis for diversity among the Mollusca. And that its specializations have been abundant is attested by the number of known species — nearly 100,000 living today and more than half that number again preserved as fossils. These species are usually arranged in six classes, the major distinctions even at this high level being provided by the shell (Table 10). In four of the groups, this protective device consists of a single part, or *valve*, but special features in each case set off the classes sharply. In the class containing the chitons, the eight-valved division of the shell results in a segmented appearance quite foreign to the other mollusks, while the two valves of the shell fish distinguish them at a glance.

Although a few modifications of the gastropods are shown in Figure 59, the innumerable specializations of that class are far beyond the scope of this book.[2] To provide a more concrete appreciation of the changes that have occurred within a single class, attention will be focused on a smaller one, the Cephalopoda.

### Diversity in the Cephalopoda.

Two good reasons besides size exist for choosing the present class to illustrate diversification in the mollusks as a whole. In the first place, the squids and octopi hold a particular fascination for most persons, and secondly, the history of the group is especially clearly documented in the fossil record.

Some of the clarity stems from the unique shell, which besides fossilizing readily, can be identified with certainty. Like that of the modern chambered nautilus, the shell is divided internally by a series of transverse *septa*, through which a tube called a *siphon* extends (Fig. 60). In addition, the exterior of the shell beneath the outermost horny covering is marked with transverse *sutures*, corresponding to the edges of the internal septa.

---

[1]M. J. Wells, "What the Octopus Makes of It: Our World from Another Point-of-View," *American Scientist*, 49:215-227, 1961. This article presents in interesting fashion some experiments concerned with sense perception and intelligence in the octopi.

[2]Sea-going slugs are described by W. M. Stephens, "Improbable Mollusk," *Natural History*, 75(7):44-49, August, 1966.

TABLE 10

*The Classes of Mollusks*

Classes

| Characteristics | Monoplacophora | Amphineura | Scaphopoda | Pelecypoda | Gastropoda | Cephalopoda |
|---|---|---|---|---|---|---|
| Shell | Single, cup-shaped | Of 8 plates or absent | Tubular, open at both ends | Bivalvular | Tubular, often spiral, sometimes flat or absent | Reduced or absent |
| Foot | Discoidal | Discoidal or rudimentary | Reduced | Wedge-shaped | Flat | Modified into 8 or more tentacles |
| Body | Segmented internally | Unsegmented | Unsegmented | Unsegmented | Unsegmented | Unsegmented |
| Gills | 5 pairs, external | 6 to 80 pairs, around foot | Absent | 2 pairs, internal | 1 pair, 1, or none; respiration sometimes by lungs or mantle | 1 or 2 pairs |
| Sense organs | Sensory tentacles | Absent | Sensory tentacles | Palpi, eyespots; sensory tentacles absent | Sensory tentacles, eyes | Eyes very well-developed; sensory tentacles absent |
| Habitats | Marine | Marine | Marine | Marine and fresh-water | Marine, fresh-water, and terrestrial | Marine |
| Common names | ——— | Chitons; solenogastres | Tooth shells; tusk shells | Clams; oysters, mussels, etc. | Snails, slugs, conchs, whelks, earshells, etc. | Squids, nautili, octopi |

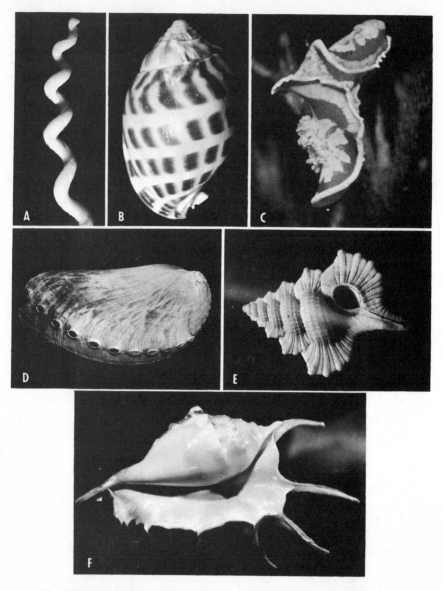

**Fig. 59.** *A few examples of diversity among gastropods. A.* The worm shell looks like a worm burrow but is actually a snail shell. *B.* The checkerboard helmet shell. *C.* Slugs, including sea slugs or nudibranches like this one, have lost the shell completely. *D.* Although the ear shells look like one half of a bivalve shell, they are actually a highly diversified type of snail. *E.* The kookaburra shell resembles that bird. *F.* The smooth spider shell, like all the foregoing, is from the South Pacific.

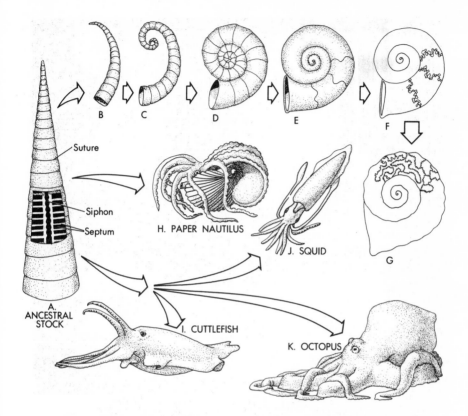

**Fig. 60.** *Paths of diversification in the Cephalopoda.* The ancestral stock produced three major lines of development still represented by living forms.

The group is first represented in the Ordovician, nearly a half billion years ago, by straight conical shells; these cone-shaped fossils, sometimes 15 feet long, have all the characteristics outlined above. Obviously still earlier forms must have existed in which the sutures, septa, and siphon were gradually developed, but nothing suggestive of these preliminary steps has been discovered as yet. The straight cones later became slightly curved and subsequently more and more strongly so, until, among still later representatives, the typical spiraled condition was attained (Fig. 60).

During Devonian times, about 100 million years later, one side branch shows the beginnings of a new modification, the purpose of which is difficult to deduce. Up this point the sutures had been straight, but with this group's advent, they began to undulate slightly. In still later fossils

**143**

the undulations were more pronounced and eventually the simple waves themselves became sinuous. Gradually these doubly sinuous sutures increased in complexity, until in the Mesozoic period, which ended 135 million years ago, they were as intricate (Fig. 60) as those found on the last survivor of this line of development, the chambered nautilus.

Other types of specializations were acquired by descendants of the Ordovician stock; as these are not well supported by fossil forms, the modern species must be used in suggesting what probably occurred. Along one path of evolution, represented today by the paper nautili, the shell is not attached to the body by muscles as is usual and is present only in the female. This is held around the body to provide protection by a specifically adapted pair of tentacles. In addition the shells serve as a depository for the eggs, in which they remain until hatched.

The third and final line of development which began in the same ancestral stock is marked by the increasing muscularity of the mantle which provides greater speed in swimming. As their ability increased to escape attack by taking flight, the shell was no longer needed for protection but became more and more a handicap. Consequently among successively higher stages it is gradually reduced in size. In early representatives the mantle then surrounded the reduced shell, so that eventually it became internal, as in the cuttlefish of today. Among still more advanced forms like the squids, the shell is reduced to a feather-like rod known as the pen, while the true octopi at the very end of the branch lack the shell entirely.

## II. THE ECHINODERMATA

Of all the phyla of animals, probably none is more peculiar than the Echinodermata. Only here is the radial type of symmetry acquired secondarily by the adults from bilaterally symmetrical larvae, and its members alone possess a hydraulic system to operate expandible tubes that serve in locomotion.

All the 8,000 known living species are bottom-dwellers in the oceans and are universally arranged into five classes (Table 11). In addition innumerable fossil forms have been described, including representatives of five extinct classes.

### Morphology

Although highly divergent from the other phyla and specialized along five separate lines, the modern echinoderms within each major division are remarkably undiversified. Perhaps this lack of important modification

TABLE 11

*The Modern Classes of Echinodermata*

| Characteristic | Classes | | | | |
|---|---|---|---|---|---|
| | Crinoidea | Holothuroidea | Asteroidea | Echinoidea | Ophiuroidea |
| Position of oral surface | Upward | On one end | Downward | Downward | Downward |
| Body form | Spherical or ovoid with numerous tentacle-like brachioles; often stalked | Elongate, cylindrical | Starlike or discoidal, with 5 or more arms | Globular or discoidal; often covered with long spines | Starlike, with 5 slender arms |
| Tube feet | Primarily food-catching; on upper surface of arms | Locomotory, not in grooves; sometimes absent | Locomotory, in grooves on oral surface of arms | Locomotory, not in groves | Reduced to sensory papillae, not in grooves |
| Endoskeleton | Of immovable plates | Of scattered ossicles | Of movable plates | Of immovable plates | Of movable plates |
| Larvae | Doliolaria | Auricularia and doliolaria | Bipinnaria and brachiolaria | Pluteus | Pluteus |

helps to account for the relative paucity of living representatives. As a consequence, attention will be confined largely to the diversities of the phylum as a whole.

In addition to the hydraulic mechanism mentioned above, which zoologists call the *water-vascular system,* and the extendible *tubefeet* (Figure 61), a number of other traits are unusual. First among these is the skeletal system. This is of the endoskeletal type, found elsewhere only among the vertebrates; in the present animals it is also distinctive in generally consisting of plates. These plates, made of calcium compounds, interlock to form a sort of shell, or *test;* in starfish and most classes the plates are movable but in the sea urchins they are rigidly attached to one another. The sea cucumbers are distinct in having the

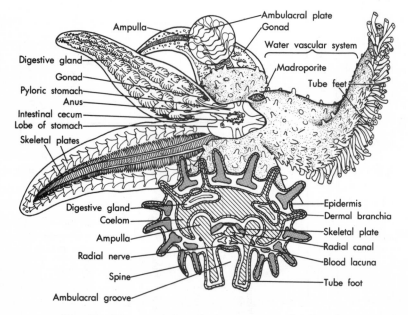

**Fig. 61.** *The morphological characteristics of echinoderms.*

plates replaced by small ossicles embedded in the dermis. This same group also lacks another feature of the skeleton present in all the others, the spiny projections on which the technical name is based (*echino,* meaning "spiny," and *derma,* "skin.").[3]

---

[3]An interesting account of echinoderms is found in A. L. Burnett, "Enigma of an Echinoderm," *Natural History,* 70(9):10-20, November, 1961.

The circulatory system is peculiar, too, for the blood, instead of flowing through vessels, travels through channels in the coelom. These channels, called *lacunae* because they lack definite walls, are especially well developed in the sea cucumbers and sea urchins, particularly in association with the digestive tract. Hence the blood more than likely aids in the distribution of digested material. Probably, along with the body wall in general, it assists also in excretion and respiration, as special organs for these functions are lacking. For many years no heart was known to exist in the echinoderms, but recently one has been demonstrated to be present in the so-called axial gland, located close to the water-vascular system.

Except in the sea cucumbers, where the tract extends throughout most of the body's length, the digestive system is quite short. Rather than the intestine providing the bulk of the system as in other animals, the stomach along with its associated glands is the largest organ. This condition stems from the manner of feeding. By way of illustration, the starfish, whose principal food consists of bivalves, forces open a mollusk shell and everts its stomach around the prey. Then the digestive fluids are poured out and the enzymes permitted to act upon the bivalve's tissues. When these are sufficiently broken down, the stomach and its enclosed digested materials are retracted into the body.

### Reproduction

Little that is distinctive exists in the basic processes of reproduction. Except in the few hermaphroditic species of sea cucumbers and brittle stars, the sexes are separate, and fertilization almost always takes place in the seas. But the larvae resulting from the fertilized eggs are most remarkable.

Although within each class distinctive larval types occur, these share far more characteristics than their diverse names may indicate (Table 11). Unfortunately, the earliest larval stages, which might resemble a trochophore, are passed within the egg, so distinctive traits do not become apparent; consequently, even the simplest actual larva upon hatching already possesses a great many modifications. The most primitive type, known as the *auricularia* and found in the sea cucumbers, shows the beginnings of one of the most peculiar traits of echinoderm larval stages, the extension of the ciliated bands into folds (Fig. 62) projecting outward from the body. In this form, as in all other echinoderm larvae, the presence of a *hydrocoel*, or water sac, is a noteworthy feature. Beyond this basic type two major trends may be considered to develop. In the first of these, oddly enough, the folds are reduced in extent, so that the cilia become arranged to form a number of nearly horizontal rows encircling the body; this stage is represented by the *doliolaria* characteristic of both the crinoids and sea cucumbers.

The second trend of development is just the opposite, for the folds become greatly extended. In the *pluteus* of the brittle stars and the sea

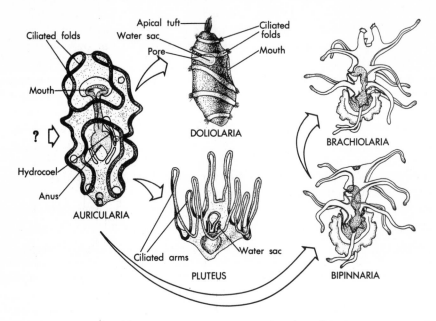

**Fig. 62.** *Diversification among echinoderm larvae.*

urchins, the ciliated lobes ultimately become so prolonged as to be armlike; four, six, or even eight, pairs of long arms may be present, each supported internally by a slender skeleton. In contrast the folds of starfish larvae do not become so prolonged as they do intricate in arrangement and number. The first larva (Fig. 62), the *bipinnaria*, possesses eleven long arms, but later develops three short preoral ones in addition and then is known as the *brachiolaria*.

Regardless of type, the larva when mature undergoes marked metamorphosis in acquiring the adult body form. During the transition, the hydrocoel ultimately develops into the unique water-vascular system that characterizes the echninoderms as a whole.

## III. THE HEMICHORDATA

Like the onychophorans, the seventy known modern species of Hemichordata provide a link between phyla that would otherwise have forever remained undetected, for these soft-bodied forms are not represented in the fossil record. Moreover, in this case, th presence of living members is of even greater importance, for the evidence of interrelationships is furnished largely by the minute larva.

### Morphology

One of the most surprising discoveries for a beginning student is that the stock whose ancestors gave rise to the phylum to which he himself belongs is today represented by worms. These *acorn worms*, which spend their lives in burrows in the ocean bottom, are striking in appearance because of a peculiar adaptation for creeping. In the place where a head is usually located a thick *proboscis* occurs (Fig. 63), the shape of which provides the basis for the common name. This organ and the elevated *collar* that lies just behind it can be greatly enlarged by inflation with water and deflated by muscular contractions. By becoming distended and contracted in alternating fashion, the two structures provide locomotion for the entire body.

The principal adult trait that relates the present taxon to the Chordata is the presence of *gill slits*, opening into the pharynx in both groups. A second feature that may indicate interrelationships is found in the

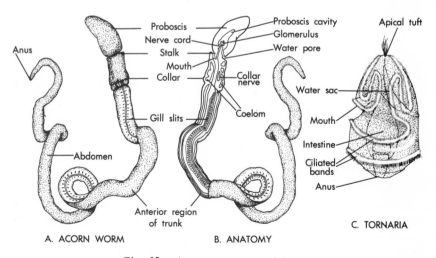

**Fig. 63.** *An acorn worm and larva.*

nervous system. Although this system consists almost entirely of nerve tracts that are not completely differentiated from the body wall, in the dorsal region of the collar there is a short hollow nerve cord like that which occurs only among the chordates.

### The Larva and Relationships

While the adult characteristics thus suggest a relationship between the Hemichordata and the Chordata, the larva is of the utmost importance in implying remote kinship with an earlier phylum. The newly hatched form of the acorn worms, called the *Tornaria,* shares many unique traits with the echinoderm larva. Among the common traits are the transparent body, undulant rows of cilia which become elevated as lobes, similar digestive tracts, and a marine habitat. In addition, each has a hydrocoel correspondingly located and of like origin. Since most of these characteristics are confined to these larvae, common descent is strongly indicated.[4]

### IV. THE CHORDATA

The end products of the annelid line of development, the Arthropoda, have gained predominance among living things of today largely through diversification into nearly countless thousands of species, for no representative has ever become very large. In contrast, the present phylum, including perhaps 70,000 living species, is relatively poor in numbers but has developed the most immense animals ever to inhabit either seas or land. Not that all its members are gigantic, for mice and hummingbirds too belong here, as well as certain fish which do not surpass an inch in length. But no terrestrial animal ever has exceeded the 90-foot *Diplodocus* in length, nor has any marine invertebrate even approached the 110-foot extent found in certain fossil sharks.

Only four structural characteristics are shared by the members of the Chordata (Fig. 64), and these are frequently confined to the larva or embryo. Generally the phylum is divided into three subphyla (Table 12), only one of which, the Vertebrata, is abundantly represented by extant forms. To show the diversification and interrelationships of the group as awhole, a synopsis of these major subdivisions will be provided first, while the following chapter will outline the most successful subphylum in greater detail.

---

[4] L. S. Dillon, "The Hydrocoel and the Origin of the Chordates," *Evolution* 19:436-466, 1965, discusses the probable importance of the water sac to both lines of descent.

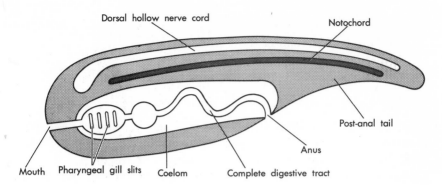

Dorsal hollow nerve cord

Notochord

Post-anal tail

Anus

Complete digestive tract

Coelom

Pharyngeal gill slits

Mouth

**Fig. 64.** *Chordate characteristics.* Just four traits are unique to the phylum Chordata.

TABLE 12

*The Subphyla of the Chordata*

| Characteristic | Subphyla | | |
|---|---|---|---|
| | Tunicata | Cephalochordata | Vertebrata |
| Notochord | Well-developed in larva, usually reduced in adult | Well-developed | Well-developed at least in embryo or larva; usually reduced in adult |
| Vertebral column | Absent | Absent | Usually present in adult |
| Nerve cord | Extends to middle of length of the larval tail; reduced in adult | Well-developed | Well-developed |
| Tunic | Usually well-developed | Absent | Absent |
| Atrium | Present | Present | Absent |
| Head | Absent | Absent | Present |
| Endostyle | Present | Present | Usually absent |
| Branchial sac | Present | Present | Absent |
| Habits | Sessile or free-floating, marine | Live in burrows, marine | Free-living, rarely semi-parasitic; marine, fresh-water, and terrestrial |
| Common names | Tunicates, ascidians, sea squirts | Lancelets | Fish, snakes, birds, mammals, toads, etc. |

151

### A. The Tunicata

Within the subphylum of the Tunicata are three major types, one of which is free-living whereas the remaining two are sessile as adults. But only the most abundant variety, the sea squirts, will be discussed here.

*Morphology*

Although the distinctive structure of the tunicates is in general clearly shown in the illustration (Fig. 65), some organs are so unusual that a brief discussion may be in order. The *tunic* is a tough chitinous coat enclosing the entire animal but permitting great flexibility. Perhaps the most striking feature of all is provided by the *branchial sac;* this basket-like structure, really the greatly enlarged pharynx, is perforated by innumerable gill slits and serves as a settling basin. As water enters the sac through the mouth and leaves by way of the slits, any organic matter suspended in it tends to settle out as the current is quieted in this voluminous organ. These particles adhere to a mucous cord secreted by the *endostyle,* an organ bearing a ciliated groove. Along this groove the cord with its adhering food bits is moved to the intestine, where the entire mass is digested. Hence, these sessile sea squirts feed by filtering sea water. Upon leaving the branchial sac, the water enters a cavity called the *atrium,* from which it passes back into the sea by way of the *excurrent siphon.*

*The Larva*

As may be seen in the illustration (Fig. 65), the larva differs strongly from the adult in morphology. In fact, the adult members of the subphylum are difficult to identify as Chordata, for such diagnostic traits as the notochord and dorsal hollow nerve cord are absent. In the tadpole-like larva, however, these as well as the postanal tail and pharyngeal gill slits are well developed. After hatching, the larva swims about actively for a period varying from a few hours to several days and then attaches itself to the substrate anterior end downward. As it adheres thus inverted, the body undergoes an extreme metamorphosis. During the alterations the whole tail is absorbed, and most of the internal organs actually rotate from bottom to top. At the same time, the nervous system is lost except for a small ganglion, and the notochord disappears entirely.

### B. The Cephalochordata

When alive the *lancelets* that comprise the subphylum Cephalochordata appear quite like small fish, but closer examination reveals the absence of eyes, opercula, and other piscine traits. Nor do the animals behave strictly as fish, for they bury themselves in sand, leaving only the anterior portion exposed. Here beneath the shallow waters of the oceans they feed by a filtering mechanism not unlike that of the tunicates.

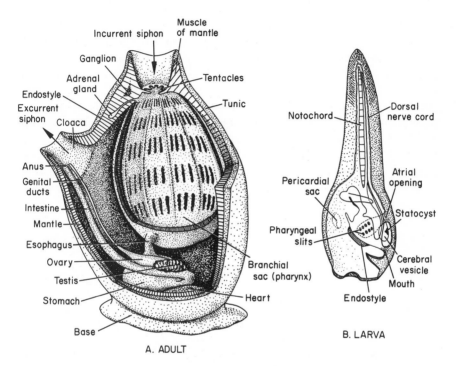

**Fig. 65.** *Structure and larva of a tunicate.* (Reproduced, with permission, from L. S. Dillon, *Principles of Animal Biology*, New York: The Macmillan Company, copyright 1965.)

*Morphology*

As in the Tunicata, the filter-feeding device consists of a *branchial sac* perforated by a series of elongate gill slits. Present, too, are the grooved *endostyle* and the mucous cord as well as numerous cilia to move the mucus and its adhering food particles into the digestive tract. As in the sea squirts, too, the circulating sea water, after exiting through the gill slits, enters an *atrium,* to leave by means of a posterior opening, but in the lancelets the pore is given the distinctive name *atriopore.*

In the life cycle a larva is present, but metamorphosis into the mature form is far less marked than in the tunicates, for the larva differs little from the adult. Here the greatest change involves a reduction in the size of the brain and in loss of the eyes. Both larva and adult have the notochord and dorsal hollow nerve cord extending the full length of the body.

### C. The Vertebrata

Though an occasional systematist consigns the members of the Vertebrata to a phylum of their own, almost all consider them a subphylum of the Chordata as here, for no sharp line of demarcation can be drawn between the vertebrates and the lower members. For one thing, not every vertebrate is equipped with a vertebral column; as shall be seen shortly, although the majority during development replace the notochord with a spinal column, in some types that organ persists throughout life. Perhaps the greatest distinction between these animals and the lower chordates lies in the absence of an atrium. Even in those vertebrates whose larvae possess an endostyle — and there are a number — the gill slits open directly to the outside, not into an atrial cavity.

# CHAPTER 11

# Diversity among the vertebrata

Probably nowhere in zoology are the processes of diversification better illustrated than among the Vertebrata. By proceeding within this taxon from the simpler to the more advanced types, a clear picture of the successive steps can be gained. First the members become increasingly adapted for an active aquatic existence; then after the seas and fresh waters have been mastered, later groups show the sequential stages in becoming better fitted for a terrestrial life.

## I. THE CYCLOSTOMATA

The eel-like members of the very first class make it clear that mere numbers of a part do not in themselves signify complexity. These primitive forms, known as hagfish and lampreys (Fig. 66), possess as many as fifteen pairs of gills in a row behind the head, whereas the more complex groups have only four or five pairs. So while at first glance the long array of gills may appear far more complicated than the smaller number, when given closer consideration the latter condition is perceived to imply relatively greater respiration per gill. Hence reduction in gill number represents advancement, because it reflects the existence of a more efficient respiratory mechanism.

*Morphology*

The members of this class are primitive in many other features. Among the several important organs that are absent is one so basic for vertebrates as a vertebral column, in place of which the notochord persists throughout life. Jaws, too, are lacking; consequently, the circular mouth cannot be opened or closed but functions as a suction disk in attaching to the fish on which these cyclostomes feed. Inside the buccal cavity and on the tongue are a number of toothlike spines with which they rasp through the flesh of their prey (Fig. 66). As bone is wanting, the entire skeleton, including the cranium, is made of cartilage and other connective tissues. Moreover, the heart is a nearly straight tube divided into two chambers (Fig. 71) and located just behind the mouth. However, an even more drastic deficiency for actively swimming vertebrates is the lack of paired appendages, universally present in all higher classes.

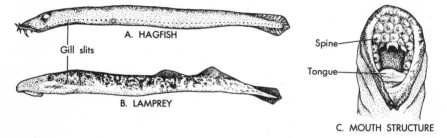

**Fig. 66.** *Representatives of the Cyclostomata.*

*Development*

Probably the greatest importance the cyclostomes hold for biology lies in the characteristic lamprey larva, called the *ammocoetes*. Many features of this developmental stage suggest that diversification among the Vertebrata may have had its origin in a simple form not unlike the lancelets. Upon hatching, the ammocoetes builds a burrow in a muddy brook bottom, within which it lives with only the head projecting. At this time the mouth is not sucker-like nor is it equipped with spines. As water circulates in by way of the mouth and out by the gill slits, minute particles, such as algae and protozoa, adhere to a mucous rope contained in a ciliated endostyle, basically identical with that of the lancelets. Within the burrow the larva lives for nearly two years, gradually increasing in length until it undergoes metamorphosis into the adult form.

## II. THE CHONDRICHTHYES

Between the foregoing early vertebrates and the next level represented by living forms, many developments occurred, most of which are not clearly shown even by fossils. Among the most important structures gained during this interval are jaws, two sets of paired fins, and vertebrae. In spite of all these additions which involve the skeleton, no true bone is as yet present, but only cartilage as before; reference to this condition is made by the technical name Chondrichthyes, that is "cartilagefish." The sharks,[1] rays, and related forms constitute this class.

### Paired Appendages

So basic are the paired appendages in vertebrate diversification that some attention needs to be devoted to them here in the first branch in which they occur. Generally these organs are accepted to have had their origin in a continuous fin fold that once encircled most of the primitive body from the dorsal to the ventral surface, where it branched onto the sides (Fig. 67). While much variation in structure exists, fundamentally

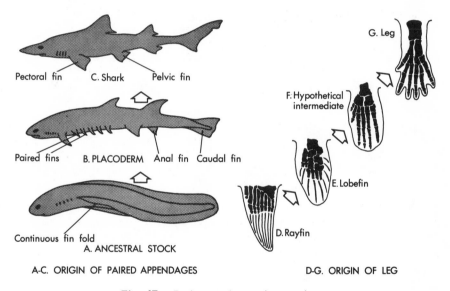

Pectoral fin  C. Shark  Pelvic fin

Paired fins  B. PLACODERM  Anal fin  Caudal fin

Continuous fin fold
A. ANCESTRAL STOCK

A-C. ORIGIN OF PAIRED APPENDAGES

G. Leg

F. Hypothetical intermediate

E. Lobefin

D. Rayfin

D-G. ORIGIN OF LEG

**Fig. 67.** *Evolution of paired appendages.*

the supportive skeleton consists of three basal elements, followed by several series of others arranged in transverse rows (Fig. 67). To the latter are attached *dermal rays* which support the flat portion of the fin,

---

[1]Interesting sidelights into these vertebrates is provided by P. W. Gilbert, "The Behavior of Sharks," *Scientific American,* July, 1962.

while the entire appendage hinges internally on an *arch*. This basic type, referred to as a *ray fin*, occurs among the true fish as well as here in the sharks and rays. In the rays, the great expansion of the pectoral appendages provides the animals with their characteristic broad, depressed shape (Fig. 68).

**Fig. 68.** *A stinging ray.*

### Other Characteristics

If the embryology of this group is to be believed, the jaws originated by modification of those cartilages that support the first pair of gill slits. While these were undergoing elaboration, related parts were being acquired that illustrate one way in which new structures may develop. The novel parts referred to are the *teeth*, without which the jaws would have remained inefficient organs of mastication indeed.

All available evidence points to the peculiar scales covering the body as the source from which teeth have been derived. The placoid scales found on all Chondrichthyes consist of minute rhomboidal platelets, each provided on the outer surface with a sharp projection. As the hard portion of the scales consists of dentine, capped with an enamel-like layer, the structural resemblance to teeth is at once apparent. One can readily imagine that, when the ancestral jaws first formed, the rough scaly skin around the mouth moved inward to assist in mastication; when the older scales wore out, replacements were provided by further inward growth of skin. By evolutionary processes the original minute scales slowly and gradually enlarged and later became embedded as teeth in the jaws. In this connection it is interesting to note that many sharks and even certain mammals of today can replace lost teeth an indefinite number of times.

The majority of sharks and rays have just five pairs of gill slits in addition to a porelike opening, the *spiracle*. The latter represents the remnant of the primitive first gill slit's upper portion; later in terrestrial vertebrates it becomes connected with the middle ear as the Eustachian tube.[2] Equipped thus with efficient organs for respiration, locomotion, and ingestion, the sharks and rays became the dominant vertebrates in the seas and maintained their supremacy for more than 100 million years. Among the 600 or more species still extant are such extremely diversified forms as hammerhead and angel sharks, sawfish, electric rays, devilfish or manta, chimaeras, and elephant-fish.

## III. THE OSTEICHTHYES

Although the sharks and their relatives were able to become highly successful in face of the lower level of competition provided by the jawless fishes that preceded them, they in turn were replaced as still better adapted fish came into existence.

### Characteristics

The successors of the Chondrichthyes are frequently given the name Osteichthyes, the bony or ray-finned fishes,[3] but no single term is universally accepted for them. As one common name implies, their skeleton usually consists of bony tissue, although some members still retain the cartilaginous condition or have reacquired it secondarily. No further

---

[2]T. S. Parsons, (ed.), "The Vertebrate Ear," *American Zoologist* 6:368-466, 1966, presents many facets of the origin and evolution of this important and complex organ.

[3]For habits and other interesting aspects of these fishes, refer to Evelyn Shaw, "The Schooling of Fishes." *Scientific American,* June, 1962; H. W. Lissman, "Electric Location by Fishes," *ibid.,* March, 1963; J. T. Ruud, "The Ice Fish," *ibid.,* November, 1965.

improvement in gill efficiency is indicated, for the same number exists as before, except that a spiracle is absent. However, a protective covering is added over the gills. This covering, the *operculum*, extends posteriorly from the cranium and serves not only for protection but also in retaining water in the gill cavity. For example, eels in migrating up rivers often need to clamber up rocks or over dry land to pass around high falls. In doing so, the opercula are closed, so that water is trapped that keeps the gills moist. The locomotive apparatus similarly shows no improvement, as the fins are still of the ray type.[4]

## IV. THE PRETERRESTRIAL TYPES

That the bony fish possess all the features essential for an existence in water is clearly demonstrated by the presence of 50,000 species on earth today. These occupy nearly every body of water of whatever size or nature, from the smallest fresh-water pond to the very depths of the oceans. Consequently, it is difficult to perceive how the vertebrates could undergo any additional major diversification in an aquatic environment. Yet several structures absent among the forms described above are needed before an existence on land could become possible.

### The Coelacantha

Among the requisites is a mechanism to provide locomotion in a terrestrial situation; hence, the predecessor's fins must include features which can be modified for the purpose. The essential fin traits are found among ancestral coelacanths, represented today by a single species discovered in recent years off the coast of east Africa. This form, *Latimeria chalumnae* (Fig. 69) which lives in the ocean depths, has secondarily lost much of the typical lobe-fin structure that its fossil forebears possessed. These had fins far more robust than those of the ray-finned fish, for the bony elements, instead of forming transverse rows, were arranged in long series (Fig. 67). How the lobe fins proved of value to the ancestral stock cannot even be guessed; perhaps they supported the body weight as the fish rested on the lake bottoms or served during migration from one pond to another. But all that is actually known is that the fins existed and that they doubtlessly played a role vital to their possessors.

---

[4]B. Curtis, *The Life Story of the Fish: His Morals and Manners*, New York: Harcourt, Brace and Company, 1949; J. R. Norman, *History of Fishes*, London: Berne, 1931; and L. P. Schultz and Edith Stern, *The Ways of Fishes*, New York: D. Van Nostrand Company, 1948, are outstanding among many books that treat the fish in an interesting manner.

**Fig. 69.** *A modern coelacanth.* The sole known species of today, *Latimeria chalumnae,* lives at considerable depths in the Indian Ocean, off the coast of east Africa. (Reproduced, with permission, from L. S. Dillon, *Principles of Animal Biology,* New York: The Macmillan Company, copyright 1965.)

## The Choanichthyes

The peculiar lungfishes, today represented by three genera in the tropical regions, show other features needed before vertebrates could venture onto dry land. Lungs instead of gills obviously must be present immediately when a terrestrial habitat is entered, but on the surface it would appear that an air-breathing mechanism could hold no value at all for a gill-bearing aquatic organism. To the contrary, even fish may require lungs under particular conditions. The Australian lungfish (*Neoceratodus forsteri;* Fig. 70), for example, occurs in lakes which become deficient in oxygen during the long dry periods of Queensland, so that it surfaces frequently to fill its lungs with fresh air. Not only do the lungs serve for emergencies, however, but are an essential supplement to the gills at all times; even in well-oxygenated water, it has recently been shown, the lungfish will perish unless permitted to surface from time to time. Its lungs, a modified swim bladder, open into the esophagus, are well supplied with blood to be oxygenated, and are sacculated internally for greater efficiency.

Similarly the African lungfish (*Protopterus annectens*) and the South American species (*Lepidosiren paradoxa*) occupy ponds or swamps which evaporate completely during frequent droughts. As the waters disappear, the lungfish construct "cocoons" in the pond bottom, made of mud cemented by mucus. In these chambers the fish remain until rains refill the pond, in the meantime breathing air which enters by way of a tubular aperture.

The technical term of the class, however, refers to a second adaptation for respiration that its members have acquired, the nostrils. While

**Fig. 70.** *The lungfish of Australia.* This fish grows to a length exceeding 3 feet and may sometimes weigh as much as 15 pounds. (Courtesy Australian News and Information Bureau.)

a nostril-like tube leading from an olfactory pore into the mouth cavity is present in several earlier groups, including the hagfishes, a special pair of tubes for respiratory purposes occurs first in this group. Moreover, the primitive two-chambered heart has been specialized to serve the lungs more efficiently, for the single atrium of the lower fishes is here subdivided by a septum to form right and left atria (Fig. 71). The latter chamber receives only oxygenated blood from the lungs whereas the former receives deoxygenated blood from the remainder of the body. Special structures, like the spiral valve in the base of the main artery, assist in preventing the two types of blood from completely mixing as they pass through the single ventricle.

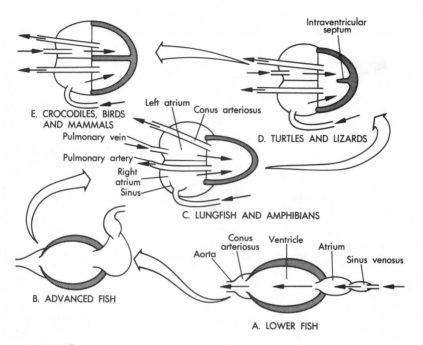

**Fig. 71.** *Some steps in the evolution of the vertebrate heart.*

## V. THE AMPHIBIA

Final emergence into a new environment, like full adaptation to aquatic situations, seemingly came about in stepwise fashion. This is suggested by the Amphibia, for its members — the frogs, toads (Fig. 72), and salamanders — are terrestrial in a limited sense only.

### Characteristics

Just one new adaptation of major importance occurs in the Amphibia, namely, the conversion of finlike appendages into true legs. The actual steps in the change are represented neither in the fossil record nor among living forms, so the illustration (Fig. 67) must be considered hypothetical. Yet the relationships are evident. In these early terrestrial vertebrates, the leg is deficient to the extent that the digits lack protective devices such as claws or nails at the tips.

Among other adaptations for a life on land is the loss of the scales that cover the bodies of fishes, probably to assist in respiration. The lungs of these animals differ only slightly from those of the lungfishes; these

**Fig. 72.** *A tree frog.* The canyon tree frog (*Hyla arenicolor*) here clings to a rock by means of the suction pads on the toes. Note that claws are absent from the digits here as in all Amphibia. (Photograph courtesy of William G. Degenhardt.)

organs are so inefficient that in many species they are supplemented with vascularized skin. Indeed the most highly diversified salamanders respire solely by means of the skin and have lost their lungs entirely. The three-chambered heart and its spiral valve likewise show little additional specialization, with the exception of being somewhat more compact.

The aquatic origin of the Amphibia is clearly indicated by their life history. With minor exceptions the eggs, protected only with layers of gelatinous material, are deposited and fertilized in water. The larva, or tadpole, similarly is nearly always aquatic, and possesses well-developed gills; this fishlike stage in becoming mature undergoes a marked metamorphosis.[5] Many adult salamanders, like the sirens, mudpuppies, and hellbenders, also spend their entire lives in the water, and most others are confined to damp places. Mature frogs for the greater part, too, spend at least as much time in water as on land. Indeed, as a group, only the toads and tree frogs can be said to be really terrestrial after attaining

[5]See E. Frieden, "The Chemistry of Amphibian Metamorphosis," *Scientific American*, November, 1963.

maturity. Perhaps as a consequence of their close tie to water, the Amphibia never became highly deversified and developed only a wormlike variety, the caecilians, in addition to the creeping salamanders and leaping frogs and toads.

## VI. THE REPTILIA

As the bond with water was broken more completely, however, the vertebrates were enabled to diversify along many different lines in the conquest of the terrestrial environment. In the Reptilia, for instance, besides the lizards, snakes, turtles, and crocodilians of today (Fig. 73), one can recall to mind the dinosaurs, pterodactyls, and other striking reptiles of past ages.

### Characteristics

Were one to choose a single adaptation that probably contributed most to liberating the terrestrial vertebrates from their earlier aquatic ties, in all likelihood the egg covering would be selected. Because the egg is now provided with a leathery or calcareous shell, it can be deposited in the earth, with the result that reproduction no longer is dependent upon bodies of water. But in developing a shell, provision also had to be made for supplying the growing embryo and young with oxygen and food and for removing waste products. For these functions a series of embryonic membranes developed. Among them are included a chorion that assists in respiration, an amnion whose liquid contents provide moisture and prevents damage to the embryo, a yolksac in which food is stored, and the allantois that receives nitrogenous wastes.

Also fundamental in enhancing adaptation for the terrestrial mode of life are improvements in both the lungs and the circulatory system to elevate respiratory efficiency. The several types of living reptiles suggest steps through which the three-chambered heart of the amphibians eventually became four-chambered. Among the most primitive modern forms, the turtles,[6] the ventricle receives both oxygenated and deoxygenated blood from the two atria as in the frog; however, here a short septum extends forward from the apex. The partially divided chamber to some extent lessens the mixing of the blood (Fig. 71). At the somewhat higher stage represented by the snakes and lizards, this interventricular septum is more extensive, and at the most advanced level, reflected by the crocodiles and alligators, it entirely divides the ventricle into two.

---

[6]A fascinating account of one species of turtle is found in A. Carr, "The Navigation of the Green Turtle," *Scientific American,* May, 1965.

**Fig. 73.** A few modern reptiles. A. This 17-foot long Australian crocodile is known to be 90 years of age. B. The tuatara, the sole surviving species of an ancient group, lives on rocks around the seas of New Zealand. (Courtesy of New Zealand National Publicity.) C. The taipan of New Guinea and northern Australia carries the most potent venom of any snake living; these young may eventually reach a length of 8 feet. (A, C. Courtesy of the Australian News and Information Bureau.) D. The gopher snake of the southwest is one of numerous species that can live in dryer areas of the world. (Courtesy of William G. Degenhardt.)

Although in the last case the four-chambered heart is perfected, mixing of blood still occurs as a result of the persistence of two aortae, one leading from each ventricle. After the one from the left ventricle carrying oxygenated blood has given off branches supplying the head, the two aortae fuse to conduct blood to the posterior end of the body. Moreover, these major vessels cross over one another near the heart; at the point of crossing a foramen exists through which intermingling also occurs to some degree.

Because of these and other improvements, the skin, freed of service in respiration, again becomes covered with protective scales. In reacquiring a coat, a new type of scale evolves, illustrating the evolutionary principle that once a structure has been lost it is never regained. Whereas among fish the body covering is derived from the dermis, in the reptiles it originates from the epidermis.

## VII. THE AVES

Although the specializations gained by the reptiles enabled them to invade territory uninhabitable for amphibians, such as the extensive desert and semidesert areas of the world, their adaptations are not the ultimate. Large regions in higher latitudes are unavailable to them, as indicated by their current absence from cold temperate and polar areas. In conquering these additional territories and in better mastering the others, two separate lines of diversity developed, one of which leads to the present class, the birds.

### Characteristics

One trait acquired by birds is a warm-blooded condition, or *endothermy*, in the establishment of which two major specializations are needed, namely, a physiological mechanism to produce an ample supply of heat and an insulating coat to prevent its loss. To provide insulation, the heat-conductive scales of the reptiles gradually became modified to feathers, which are poor conductors.

It should not be thought that the feathers were acquired mainly to serve as heat-insulators; their heat-preserving ability was a secondary function, although of the greatest importance, for the earliest birds were largely tropical. Since the very first bird known from the fossil record, *Archeopteryx*, is equipped with these structures, their principal use in flight is indicated then as now. Flight, indeed, is the prime characteristic of the Aves as a whole, and, though a few running types like the ostriches and cassowaries (Fig. 74) and swimming specialists like the penguins

**Fig. 74.** *A few highly specialized birds. A.* A wingless kiwi leaving its burrow at nightfall. (Courtesy of New Zealand National Publicity.) *B.* The cassowary from tropical parts of Australia is one of several large flightless birds of the world. C. The lyrebird, also from Australia, is one of the most striking birds of today; moreover, it is remarkable for its skill as a mimic. (*B, C,* courtesy of Australian News and Information Bureau.)

have lost the ability to fly, the success of this class can be attributed chiefly to this trait.[7]

Nearly all the major characteristics of birds are directed toward improvement in flying ability, especially by increased buoyancy. To this end heavy teeth have been replaced by a light horny beak, and the long bony tail of reptiles has been almost completely lost. Bones have become lightened by reducing the thickness of the ossified shafts, and between the internal organs are air sacs connected to the lungs. Nitrogenous wastes are reduced to a semisolid condition and do not accumulate in a bladder, so that organ has been lost.

---

[7]Some other adaptations of birds are discussed in E. G. F. Sauer, "Celestial Navigation by Birds." *Scientific American*, August, 1958, and W. H. Thorpe, "The Language of Birds," *ibid.*, October, 1956.

More direct improvements to flight also exist. Powerful muscles have become developed to move the wings, for support of which a broad keel is present among higher forms. Since great expenditures of energy occur during flight, an efficient oxygen supply is a necessity. Consequently, one of the two aortae of the reptilian stock is lost, that on the left side, so that the right aorta delivers oxygenated blood to the entire body.

These adaptations, together with nesting habits that insure a high survival rate of the young, have enabled modern birds to exist and reproduce on the lands from pole to pole. Forests, grasslands, deserts, ponds, swamps, and even the seas have their share of occupants in the form of these highly diversified vertebrates.

## VIII. THE MAMMALIA

Yet except for such forms as the auks and penguins, the birds have conquered areas of extreme climatic conditions largely by living there only during the more favorable periods for reproductive purposes. After breeding is completed, their powers of flight are employed to escape the rigors of the climate. In lacking the ability to migrate over long distances, the mammals that constitute the second major line derived from the reptiles have become more strictly adapted to the regions they occupy.

### Characteristics

Much diversification among mammals is based on traits similar to those of birds. Endothermy likewise exists here, and an insulating cover is derived from the epidermal scales of reptiles in comparable fashion. Instead of feathers, however, the insulating mechanism is hair, and unique sweat glands assist in temperature control by cooling the skin when necessary.

Improvements in respiration and circulation are also prominent features among the mammals. Probably the most noteworthy adaptation that enhances respiratory efficiency is the diaphragm. This muscular organ, in conjunction with the movable ribs, enables the lungs to empty and fill more completely than is possible in other vertebrates. As in the birds, the four-chambered heart has only a single aorta, but in the present group the left aorta remains while the right one is lost. Consequently, the two organs, although superficially alike, are considered to have been separately derived, starting with the partially septate condition of the ancestral stock.

No single locomotory specialization marks the mammals as the wings do among birds, for the legs are highly diversified in function. Here probably the outstanding modification is found in reproductive traits, which begin, interestingly enough in nest-building habits not too dissimilar from those of avians. The most primitive mammals of today are the monotremes, which forms, including the duck-billed platypus and spiny anteater (Fig. 75), are egg layers. The eggs of the platypus are covered with a leathery shell quite like that of turtles and are deposited in a nest enclosed in a subterranean burrow. Only after hatching can improvement over reptilian methods be noted, for the young are then fed milk. However, as nipples have not been developed as yet, the young obtain the milk by way of hair tufts along which the secretion flows. In the spiny anteater no nest is constructed, for the thin membrane-covered egg is deposited in a pouch; here it hatches and the young feeds on milk, using hair tufts as in the other monotreme.

Among the marsupials the pouch is developed along different lines in the two sexes, in females serving much as in the last animal discussed and in males becoming highly modified to form a scrotal sac in which the testes are carried. The females of the kangaroo, cuscus, wombat, and other marsupials (Fig. 75) show some of the early stages in the development of higher mammalian traits. The egg, now entirely devoid of a shell and yolk, is retained in the uterus, where the embryo develops while supplied food by way of a simple placenta. After an intrauterine period that varies from eleven to twenty-one days, depending upon the species, the young, after being born, climb into the pouch and attach to true nipples like those of the higher groups.

In the higher levels represented by the placental mammals the intrauterine period is greatly prolonged so that the young are well developed before birth. Within the uterus the embryo and fetus are supplied food and oxygen by a more complex placenta formed by modification of certain embryonic membranes, usually the chorion and allantois.

Much more marked diversification (Fig. 76) is found in the present class than in the other terrestrial vertebrates, based primarily on specializations of the legs and teeth. Many rodents and shrews, though feeding above ground, reproduce and sleep in burrows, while the moles spend much of their lives in tunneling through the soil. Squirrels, monkeys, and tree-kangaroos are adapted to an arboreal existence, while horses, deer, and cattle graze openly upon the land. Many others, like the seals, whales, porpoises, and dugongs, have resumed strictly aquatic habits to such an extent that some of them have regained an appearance not too unlike their fishlike ancestors, and adaptations even for a birdlike

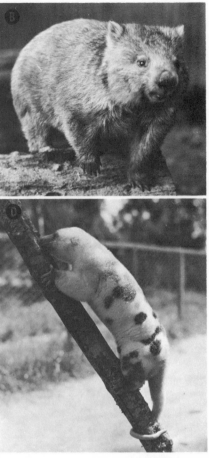

**Fig. 75.** *A monotreme and several marsupials.* All monotremes and all marsupials, aside from opossums and like types, are from the Australia-New Guinea region. *A.* The platypus daily consumes nearly its own body weight in worms and other fresh-water life; it and the several species of echidna are the only egg-laying mammals today. *B.* Wombats, one of the less familiar marsupials, resemble groundhogs in living habits. *C.* In parts of this region, tree-kangaroos correspond in habits to monkeys in other tropical portions of the world. *D.* The cuscus is one of the phalangers, more commonly known as the possums in Australia. (All courtesy of Australian News and Information Bureau.)

171

**Fig. 76.** *Some African examples of mammalian diversity.* No continent has the variety of mammal life that exists in Africa. *A.* A black rhinoceros and *B* a family of warthogs from South Africa. (Courtesy of the Natal Parks Board.) *C-D.* The national reserves in east Africa abound in wild life, such as the elephants and numerous antelopes, including the kobs shown here. (Photographs by permission of the Ministry of Information, Broadcasting, and Tourism, Uganda.) *E.* A young zebra. (Courtesy of the Natal Parks Board.)

aerial existence have been acquired by bats.[8] But these and other diversifications of the mammals are too familiar to require enumeration here.

---

[8]Among innumerable articles on mammals, the following are especially pertinent: K. Breeden, "Fructivorous Fliers," *Natural History* 73(5):26-33, May, 1964; V. Reynolds, "The Man of The Woods," *ibid.* 73(1):44-51, January, 1964; C. Ray, "Locomotion in Pinnipeds," *ibid.* 72(3):10-21, March, 1963.

These vertebrates, then, are the last examples of animal diversity that can be discussed in this brief synopsis. Though only animals still living today have been touched upon, they amply indicate the wide range of the specializations that have come into existence during the perhaps three billion years of life's history. What new developments will occur during the next three billion cannot even be guessed, but it is difficult to perceive how any of a more fascinating nature will arise than those now extant or those that have come and gone during geological ages past.

# Index